experimenting
with the
MICROSCOPE

By
DIETER KRAUTER

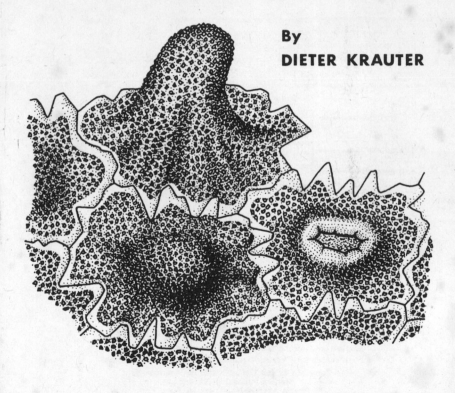

Oak Tree Press Ltd. London, Melbourne and Cape Town

OTHER BOOKS OF INTEREST

THE MICROSCOPE—AND HOW TO USE IT
MIRACLE DRUGS and the NEW AGE OF MEDICINE
WHAT'S NEW IN SCIENCE

English language edition © 1963, German edition © 1959, 1954
by Franckh'sche Verlagshandlung, W. Keller & Co., Stuttgart

Published in the United States of America by
Sterling Publishing Co., Inc.,
419 Fourth Avenue, New York 16, New York
Published in the British Empire by Oak Tree Press, Ltd., London
Manufactured in the United States of America

Contents

Preface

This book was written for the amateur microscopist who wants to try out his hobby practically. The field of applied microscopy is so immensely vast that a strict selection had to be made—and naturally, even then the areas broached here could not be treated exhaustively. A little book of this sort does not aim to compete with technical literature, but instead to offer the interested microscopist stimulation to work on his own.

The author wishes to thank Marianne Das and Dale Cunningham for assisting in the translation of this book.

DIETER KRAUTER

Before You Begin

This book assumes a knowledge of the elementary use of the microscope. It begins with a refresher course in microscopic technique, dealing with the most important methods and procedures. If you feel that you do not need this refresher, go right on to Chapter 2, knowing that you can always turn back to the first chapter if you are uncertain.

1.

Hints on Microscope Technique

Experience shows that even seasoned microscopists cannot have complete command of the most commonly used methods for fixing and staining. Therefore, it seems justified to describe briefly the most important techniques and manipulations here.

FIXING

Dead substances, such as plant fibres, wood, etc., which have been stored for long periods of time, and supporting tissues from animals can be worked up without special preliminary treatment. On the other hand, if you make permanent preparations of living tissue, you must be careful to retain the structures of cells and tissue in a condition which resembles as nearly as possible its condition during life. You have to avoid crude artifacts (artificial features or structures resulting from processing) when you kill (i.e., treat by fixing) cells or tissue, and hold shrinkage and other changes to a minimum during subsequent treatment. Consequently, you must treat fresh tissues with certain solutions which kill them and preserve their shape at the same time.

Section Fixing

Plant objects are usually studied fresh, that is, unfixed. Once in a while, however, you will want to keep an especially fine section. Unfortunately, such individual sections are even more difficult to fix than an entire piece of an organ. The author uses the following fixing mixture for sections of plant organs:

Lugol's solution ....6.0 cc.
90% alcohol ....3.0 cc.
Glacial acetic acid......0.25 cc.

Lugol's solution is made as follows:
Potassium iodide...... 6 gm.
Iodine .... 4 gm.
Distilled water ....100 cc.

NOTE: For all practical purposes, one millilitre (ml.) may be regarded as the exact equivalent of one cubic centimetre (cc.). Actually, due to experimental errors in establishing the original standards, 1 ml.= 1.000028 cc.

· Microscopists rarely prepare unfixed sections of animal organs. They can be fixed in formalin (1 part of commercial 40% formaldehyde solution plus 9 parts of well or tap water) and finally washed off in distilled water. Benda's solution of chromic, osmic, and acetic acids is more suitable.

BENDA'S SOLUTION:
1% chromic acid ....15 cc.
2% osmic acid (osmium tetroxide)...... 4 cc.
Glacial acetic acid .... 3 drops

After fixing in this solution, wash off the sections in well water or non-chlorinated tap water.

Flemming's solution (strong) could be substituted here, but in fixing sections Benda's solution is better, since it contains less acetic acid. With Flemming's solution, the fixation is primarily achieved by the acetic acid, whereas the more slowly penetrating osmic acid acts later only.

The mixture is also suitable for fixing algae, fungi, and many protozoa. The time required for fixing depends upon the thickness of the object, 10 minutes being enough for thin sections. Transfer the section from the fixing mixture to a 0.25% solution of sodium thiosulphate in distilled water. Leave the sections in this until the yellow coloration caused by the iodine has completely faded again, a minimum of 3 minutes. Finally wash it off in distilled water.

Whole-Mount Fixing

Fixing small pieces of the organs to be examined is more commonly used than fixing sections. In general, note the following points: The volume of fixative should be at least 50 times the volume of the small piece of the organ to be fixed. Place the object into the solution on some glass wool or suspend it, e.g., in a staining sieve (see p. 37), into the solution so that the fluid can penetrate well. The object must be completely saturated with the fixative. On the other hand, it should not remain in it longer than is absolutely necessary; therefore, select the smallest possible pieces for fixing. It is best for beginners to determine how deeply the fixing solution has penetrated by cutting the object. In all cases, the fixative must be washed off thoroughly again after fixing. Do this in alcohol (spirit) or water, depending upon what solution you used. Discard solutions which have been used and never use them a second time.

Of the numerous fixatives which are known, only the most familiar can be selected here. Since every fixative produces certain artifacts, it is necessary to try out several fixing methods on the same object for the most accurate studies.

ALCOHOL: Highly concentrated ethyl alcohol is popular because it is very easy to use. Place fresh objects in 96% ethyl alcohol (or preferably in absolute alcohol, 100% water-free) and allow them to remain there for 4 to 12 hours depending upon their size. If you want to embed them in paraffin or celloidin afterwards, transfer them through 90% and 80% alcohol into 70% alcohol, in which the objects can be stored.

Pure alcohol is one of the poorest fixatives. It is inadvisable to use alcohol at all for animal tissue, and for plant tissue it should be considered only for general preparations.

FORMALIN: In microtechnique, formalin or formol is understood to be a 35 to 40% solution of formaldehyde in water. This commercially available solution is diluted again with tap water for fixing. Formalin is a reasonably good fixative, especially for animal objects. Since formalin is very inexpensive, can be transported easily (on field trips, for example), and is also stable at a dilution ready for use, there are good reasons why it is widely employed. For fixing, it is best to dilute formalin in a 1 : 9 ratio with tap water. Fixing requires 1 to 2 days. Then wash the objects off in tap water. (Only in special cases should formol be diluted with distilled water.)

BOUIN'S FLUID: The fixative specified by Bouin is equally suitable for both plant and animal objects. It is one of the best fixing solutions and is preferable to the two already mentioned in almost all cases. The individual components of Bouin's solution should be mixed only immediately before use. Combine the following substances:

A saturated aqueous solution of picric acid......15 cc.
Formalin .... 5 cc.
Glacial acetic acid .... 1 cc.

Fixing requires 5 hours to 2 days, depending upon the size of the object. In this case, wash off the fixative directly in 70% alcohol, changing it until the alcohol no longer displays yellow coloration, but at least 3 times in 24 hours.

TRICHLOROACETIC ACID: Good results are obtained by fixing in 7% trichloroacetic acid, but Bouin's solution or one of the trichloroacetic acid mixtures cited below is usually preferable to pure trichloroacetic acid. The object is fixed for 1 to 12 hours and washed off in several changes of 90% alcohol.

HEIDENHAIN'S SUSA: Except for Romeis' mixture, which is mentioned next, susa is undoubtedly one of the most reliable fixing solutions which can be recommended for animal objects in particular. Even ultrafine structures are fixed true to form. Susa is made of the following:

Mercuric chloride .... 4.5 gm.
Sodium chloride .... 0.5 gm.
Trichloroacetic acid .... 2.0 gm.
Distilled water ....80.0 cc.
Glacial acetic acid .... 4.0 cc.
Formalin (40% formaldehyde)......20.0 cc.

The object is fixed for 1 to 24 hours and washed off in 90% alcohol which has been changed at least 3 times in the course of 24 to 48 hours.

ROMEIS' FIXATIVE: The solution recommended by Romeis gives very similar results to those of susa solution and is used in the same manner. It is more or less a matter of taste as to which of the two fixatives is preferred. Combine the following:

Saturated aqueous solution of mercuric chloride......25 cc.
5% solution of trichloroacetic acid ....20 cc.
Formalin .... 5 cc.

Susa and Romeis' solutions contain mercuric chloride and are therefore very toxic (for that matter, all fixing solutions are poisons). Consequently, the utmost caution should be observed in using such solutions.

After fixing in solutions containing mercuric chloride, you have to iodize the objects so that no interfering balls of mercury can form later. Add enough Lugol's solution to the alcohol used in washing off the object so that it takes on a cognac or dark tea coloration.

PFEIFFER'S MIXTURE: This solution is especially suitable for botanical purposes. Animal tissue is more expediently fixed with one of the other fixatives. Composition:

Formalin ....100.0 cc.
Purified wood vinegar......100.0 cc.
Methyl alcohol...............100.0 cc.

The fixative is washed off with water or dilute alcohol.

NAVASCHIN'S MIXTURE: Excellent for delicate plant tissue, as for any careful botanical studies—especially embryonic tissue (root tips, vegetation cone). It should be noted that it is difficult to stain objects which have been fixed in this mixture with haematoxylin stains, but safranin stains are very successful. Composition:

1% chromic acid solution......10 parts
Glacial acetic acid .... 1 part
Formalin .... 4 parts

Formalin should be added only immediately before use. In any case, it is best to combine the mixture only a very short time before fixing.

Fixing requires 24 hours or more. Wash off the fixative for several hours in running tap water or change the water frequently. Then transfer the object into several changes of 30% alcohol. Important: only small pieces can be fixed in this mixture.

DECALCIFICATION

Quite often the microscopist is confronted with the task of having to cut material which contains lime; such as, bones or animals with calcareous (i.e., lime-containing) shells. Such objects are decalcified after fixing. Only one technique of decalcifying, which the author has found to be extremely useful, will be mentioned here in detail.[1]

Fix the object to be decalcified in susa or by Romeis' technique (see above). Transfer it immediately from the fixative into 5% trichloroacetic acid to which approximately 10% formol has been added. Trichloroacetic acid decalcifies rapidly and hardly changes the tissue. It is difficult to specify the time required for decalcification. For example, the fish, guppy (*Lebistes reticulatus*), which is 2 cm. long, is completely decalcified after remaining for 2 days in trichloroacetic acid.

Transfer the object from the trichloroacetic acid into 90% alcohol and change several times to wash out the acid.

SECTIONING

You must prepare thin sections in order to be able to observe opaque objects under the microscope. In general, sections of plant objects should

---

1 This method is taken from B. Romeis, *Mikroskopische Technik*. R. Oldenbourg-Verlag, Munich, 1948.

not be thicker than 40 microns (μ), and sections of animal organs not thicker than 20μ ($1\mu = 1/1{,}000$ mm.). You can section most plant tissues as well as hard animal tissues freehand, but especially delicate tissues are ordinarily sectioned with a special cutting apparatus, the microtome. Modern microtomes produce sections as thin as 1μ. Unfortunately, the really useful microtomes are expensive; therefore, the amateur microscopist will usually have to be satisfied with freehand sections or with a cheaper hand microtome. However, a method will be described below which will enable you to obtain useful sections of delicate plant and animal tissues. Even with this method you cannot avoid the somewhat complicated embedding procedures which are required for microtome technique.

Freehand Sectioning

Hard plant organs can be cut when they are fresh without preliminary treatment. Soft plant organs, which are rich in water, must be hardened in alcohol before sectioning—in some cases after preliminary fixing.

The object is squeezed between two thin cork discs which are held with the thumb and index finger of the left hand. Now cut off the uppermost layer of the cork discs and the object with a good straight razor—by pulling, not pressing—so that a smooth cut surface is produced. Now place the edge of the razor on the surface to be cut and pass the razor over it. When the razor cuts into a suitable place on the object, continue drawing it evenly and carefully without any pressure until the section lies on the razor-blade. (Cut carefully towards yourself, not away from yourself.) To be sure, you will not obtain complete sections through the object in this way, but you will have sufficiently thin fragments from which to reconstruct the entire cross-section or longitudinal section. Remove the sections from the razor-blade with a camel's-hair brush and transfer them into a watch-glass with water. You are strongly advised always to prepare several sections, since not every section prepared will be thin enough for microscopic examination.

The freehand cutting technique requires some practice. At the beginning many microscopists are very disappointed with their sections. But increasing experimentation will make the results better and better. Even the professional microscopist with a microtome at his disposal will prefer freehand sectioning in many cases, because it saves the time required for preparing sections with the microtome. For example, almost all of the sections of plant objects which are reproduced in this book have been drawn from freehand sections.

Instead of using small cork discs to hold the object, you can punch out small cylinders with a cork punch. The cork cylinder is split, and the object is squeezed into the crack. Elderberry pith can be used to hold very soft and delicate objects.

The condition of the straight razor is the determining factor for success in freehand sectioning. A razor with an edge you could sit on will never produce usable sections. Male microscopists are advised, if they can, to shave every day with a straight instead of with a safety razor. In this way they will obtain the fingertip feel which is indispensable for the microscopist, and at the same time they will have a lasting impression of what good care a straight razor needs.

The straight razor must be stropped before sectioning and sharpened extremely evenly, using a solid, not a flexible support. Procedures are described in Stehli, *The Microscope — and How to Use It.*

In principle you could use any straight razor. Naturally, razors which have been manufactured especially for microscopy are particularly suitable. They are ground so that they are flat on one side of the blade and hollow-ground on the other. With these instruments you can skim across the back of the razor a special whetstone which guarantees that a certain optimum sharpening angle is maintained during sharpening and whetting.

A good, unused safety razor-blade in a holder (or a single-edged blade) can be used in place of a straight razor, and this has the advantage of requiring no lengthy honing and stropping; the blade is merely changed when dull. Many microscopists obtain excellent sections with a razor-blade. The author himself prefers the straight razor.

Sectioning with the Microtome

Unfortunately it is impossible to go into all of the different types of commercially available microtomes in more detail here. Generally, the firms which manufacture microtomes give instructions for the use of their type of microtome. Anyone who needs detailed instructions on microtome technique will find them in larger works on microscopic technique.[2]

Correct embedding is of decisive importance for ease in cutting an object with a microtome. That is, untreated biological objects can be cut by the microtome only in exceptional cases. Usually they must be saturated with a substance of suitable consistency to be readily cut. Such substances are, in particular, celloidin and paraffin. Since it is very tedious, embedding

---

[2] *Mikroskopische Technik* is a work that cannot be recommended highly enough to the advanced microscopist and is absolutely indispensable to anyone who wants to study animal tissue more thoroughly —see 1.

in celloidin is carried out only in special cases at present. Let us consider embedding in paraffin, especially since this method of embedding can also be used for freehand sectioning. Paraffin is insoluble in water and alcohol. But since the objects must be completely saturated with paraffin they must be placed first in a liquid in which paraffin is soluble. Romeis recommends benzene in particular as such a clearing medium. However, the novice will have better results with pure oil of turpentine than with benzene which makes the objects brittle if not used quite properly.

DEHYDRATION

First, the fixed and washed objects must be carefully dehydrated. Usually they are dehydrated with alcohol. However, if you transfer pieces of an organ directly into absolute (completely water-free) alcohol, they shrink considerably. For this reason use an alcohol series; that is, transfer the objects, for example, from water into 20% alcohol, from this into 40% alcohol, into 60%, 80%, 90% 96%, and finally into 100% (absolute) alcohol. It is all right to use methyl alcohol for the alcohol series up to 90% alcohol. Methyl alcohol can be estimated to be about 94%.

The dilution of alcohol is very simple, since it does not matter if you are a few percentage points off in this case. Fill a measuring cylinder with as many cc. of 94% alcohol as the percentage of the desired alcohol solution (for example, to obtain 40% alcohol, 40 cc.) and fill it up to 94 cc. with distilled water. For absolute alcohol, it is expedient to use isopropyl alcohol which is considerably less expensive than ethyl alcohol. The staining sieve (see p. 37) is particularly suitable for transferring objects from one liquid to another. It is advisable to suspend it in tall specimen bottles (30 x 80 mm. or 43 x 50 mm.) which can be stoppered with a cork.

You must estimate the time to keep objects in each solution of the alcohol series in such a way that complete equalization of the concentration within the small piece of the organ can occur. For a piece with edges which are 1 cm. long, 4 to 5 hours in each are sufficient for concentrations up to 60%. For concentrations higher than 60%, it is better to figure on a day in each. In absolute alcohol, which should be changed at least once and preferably twice, the objects should remain for two 24-hour periods (or longer) if isopropyl alcohol is used.

You can transfer them directly from the absolute alcohol into pure oil of turpentine, which is soluble both in absolute alcohol and in paraffin. If you do not first completely remove traces of alcohol in the objects, places can form which section poorly. For this purpose, insert 2 to 3 portions of methyl benzoate between the absolute alcohol and oil of turpentine. Leave the objects in the first portion of methyl benzoate until they have become translucent and sink. They should be kept in both the second and third portions of methyl benzoate 6 to 12 hours, but even 1 to 2 days will not hurt. Next follow with another 3 portions of oil of turpentine, keeping them in each about 4 to 8 hours. Finally, transfer them from the last portion of oil of turpentine directly into melted paraffin. It is advisable not to use the individual liquids too often. For example, the first portion of oil of turpentine should be discarded after it has been used twice, the second then used as the first, the third as the second, and new oil of turpentine should be used for the last portion.

If you have used a fixative which was rinsed off with alcohol, it is obvious that you should begin the step-by-step dehydration with the next solution in the alcohol series. For example, after fixing in Bouin's fluid— which is washed off with 70% alcohol—start with 80% alcohol.

Many of you may be deterred from such tedious work in dismay when you read of the many steps which precede embedding in paraffin. Actually the methods we have to use are not ideal. First, they require a very long time. Second, plant objects become extremely hard and brittle when they are kept for such a long time in water-free liquids and consequently become difficult to section. Several useful rapid methods for paraffin embedding have been discovered recently which shorten the operation considerably; by these means plant objects can also be sectioned very smoothly. However, these methods involve using dangerous chemicals, poisonous fumes, and special equipment; also it should be emphasized that there is hardly a single rapid method which retains the very fine structures as well as the methods described, which have been tested for decades.

Many microtechnicians recommend the use of pyridine for dehydration before paraffin embedding. (According to the author's experiences, the method is really good, but the unpleasant scent of pyridine is objectionable.) After washing with water or alcohol suspend the objects in pyridine. The pyridine container must be well sealed with a glass stopper. Cover the bottom of the container with a layer of sodium or potassium hydroxide. The water contained in the objects sinks to the bottom and is absorbed by the potassium hydroxide there. Dehydration which is carried out in this way is extremely rapid and relatively gentle. Small pieces are dehydrated after 1 to 2 hours, but in no case should they be kept in pyridine for longer than 6 hours, for the shrinkage is too great then. For this reason you should select objects which are large enough. Transfer them from pyridine directly into 3 changes of the clearing agent. It is also suitable to use oil of turpentine in this case. Allow it to act for 1 to several hours, depending upon the size of the objects.

Renew the layer of potassium hydroxide in the pyridine container when it begins to melt. The pyridine itself can be used again and again.

Ethyl cellosolve (the ethyl ether of ethylene glycol) is a very useful solvent for microscopy. Methyl cellosolve can be substituted, but is much less satisfactory.

Ethyl cellosolve is soluble in water, alcohol, oil of turpentine, xylene, benzene, and in many solvents. You can transfer objects from water or alcohol into ethyl cellosolve. They should remain there for 10 to 24 hours, depending upon their size. (Change at least twice.) You can transfer portions of organs from the ethyl cellosolve directly into oil of turpentine where they should remain for a total of about 12 hours. (Change the oil of turpentine several times.) Ethyl cellosolve is preferable to pyridine since it does not have an unpleasant scent.

EMBEDDING

Embedding the object in paraffin is another special problem. Depending upon the size of the objects let them remain in liquid paraffin for 5 to 24 hours. The paraffin should not become warmer than 60° C. Objects are usually embedded in paraffin in an incubator. However, anyone who does not own an incubator need not forgo paraffin embedding. The following description of paraffin embedding by means of a carbon filament lamp is satisfactory even for fastidious requirements, and can be carried out even under the most primitive laboratory conditions.

Fill a porcelain crucible with liquid paraffin with a melting point of 54–56° C. and let it solidify. Mount a carbon filament lamp over the crucible in such a way that its lower edge is still several centimetres above the surface of the paraffin. The upper layers of paraffin will be melted several centimetres deep by the heat of the carbon filament lamp. However, if the lamp is properly adjusted, an unmelted layer will always remain on the bottom. Place the objects coming from oil of turpentine in the paraffin; they will sink to the bottom and then lie at the boundary between melted and unmelted paraffin. Thus, they can never be heated appreciably above the melting point of paraffin. In this way the objects can be left in liquid paraffin as long as you desire. It should further be noted that objects which have once been embedded in solid paraffin and are later placed in liquid paraffin provide very poor sections in general.

It is advisable that paraffin used for embedding should only be used once. If clearing agents other than oil of turpentine are employed, the paraffin must even be changed at least once while the objects are being saturated.

Paraffin which can be sectioned especially well can be obtained if you add 5% (not more) beeswax to commercial paraffin, heat it until white fumes rise (caution: inflammable), and finally filter it. It is advisable to carry out this procedure in the home-made hot air sterilizer described on p. 191. In this case you need not be so very cautious about the inflammability of paraffin fumes.

COATING

Finally, the object which is saturated with paraffin must still be surrounded with a coat of paraffin. Lubricate a small glass container well with glycerine and fill it with the unused paraffin. The paraffin should have a temperature of about 60° C. Then a thin layer of solid paraffin will form immediately on the bottom of the colder glass container on which the paraffin-saturated object is placed. Then put the glass container into a larger dish. Pour cold water into the large dish until the water reaches the edge of the vessel containing paraffin. When the surface of the paraffin has also solidified, the whole is flooded with water. After a few minutes the paraffin block can easily be removed from the embedding vessel. It must still be cut into a suitable form with a hot razor-blade. You can store the paraffin blocks for unlimited periods of time.

Water-soluble embedding substances—polyethylene glycols—have recently come into use. Objects can be transferred into them directly from water. According to experience up to the present time, they are still not entirely satisfactory. In no case can they replace paraffin.

STRAIGHTENING

Cement the thin sections, which have been produced from paraffin blocks with the microtome, to a microscope slide. Coat a clean slide with an extremely thin layer of albumin-glycerine (equal volumes of egg-white and glycerine with the addition of a few bits of camphor) or serum-glycerine. Place the sections on it with a fine brush, drop distilled water on them so that the sections just float, and warm carefully over a small flame. The sections which were previously wrinkled become straightened in this process. When the sections have become quite smooth, allow the water to run off and place the microscope slide vertically on one edge to dry. The paraffin should on no account begin to melt during the process of straightening the sections. It is expedient to carry out the drying at an elevated temperature (about 40° C.), either near a heater or in an incubator. The sections can be treated further only when they are completely dry, as a rule only on the following day.

Heat the sections which are straight and completely dried over the flame to the point the paraffin just begins to melt. Heating over 60° C. is harmful. Then the albumin which was used for cementing coagulates, and the sections adhere firmly to the slide if they fit closely to the glass. Now place the entire slide in a jar of xylene in which the paraffin is soluble. After a few minutes transfer it into absolute isopropyl alcohol, from this into 90% alcohol into 80—60—40% alcohol, and finally into distilled water. It should remain in each member of the series for about 3 minutes, but longer will not do any harm. It is better not to use the alcohol series which was used to dehydrate the whole, uncut object for the sections.

If the objects have been fixed in a fluid containing mercuric chloride you must still iodize the sections. Then add enough Lugol's solution to the 80% alcohol so that it takes on the coloration of dark tea. The sections remain in iodine-alcohol until observation under the microscope shows that there is no longer a precipitate of mercury, but at least for 5 minutes. Treat the iodized sections as usual. However, do not transfer them directly from 40% alcohol into distilled water, but first into a freshly prepared 0.25% solution of sodium thiosulphate. This removes traces of iodine which would destroy most stains in a short time. Then transfer them from the sodium thiosulphate solution into distilled water before staining.

Freehand Sectioning of Embedded Material

You can utilize the advantages of microtome technique even without a microtome. Many microscopists believe that they could never dare to section animal organs or delicate plant tissue without a microtome. That is an error. The old masters of animal and human histology (study of tissues) knew how to prepare with a straight razor extremely thin sections of material which were not even embedded, but only hardened in alcohol. The entire edifice of histology was founded on the results obtained with the very primitive methods of those days. You can embed especially delicate tissue with small cells in paraffin, just as for microtome technique. To obtain good freehand sections from paraffin blocks it is absolutely indispensable to add beeswax, as described above, since in that way the paraffin becomes more pliant and does not crumble so easily.

Cut the paraffin block cast with a sharp razor according to the directions above in such a way that the object is still surrounded only by a thin paraffin mantle, 2 to 3 mm. wide. Then cement the block to the tabletop with a drop of liquid paraffin, and prepare to cut with a sharp scalpel. Grasp the straight razor at the far end with the left hand, at the inner end with the right hand, put it on the surface to be cut, and suddenly press it through the object. In other words, in cutting the paraffin block you should press the razor through the object. (This method would be very wrong in cutting a fresh object or one which had been hardened in alcohol.) The razor should cut only into the surface under the pressure of its own weight; additional pressure from top to bottom would be wrong.

If the sections curl very much, then they are certainly too thick. Good sections should be almost transparent and lie almost level on the razor blade. The beginner is advised to examine several sections he has cut in oil of turpentine by way of trial. Oil of turpentine dissolves out the paraffin very quickly, and you can get an idea of the thickness of the section, although fine structures will be visible only in stained and mounted preparations.

You can work in the same way with a hand microtome. Cement the paraffin block onto a wooden block, and clamp this into the object clamp of the hand microtome. Push the razor from where it lies on the glass plate of the microtome through the paraffin block with a sudden thrust. (These methods are not to be used for non-embedded objects, through which the blade is *drawn* both with the hand microtome and in freehand sectioning.)

Sections obtained by hand are treated further in the same way as microtome sections. However, since the sections will be thicker than microtome sections, they cannot be cemented on the slide as securely as the latter. For this reason they have to be coated with an extremely thin film of collodion, as follows.

Paraffin is removed with xylene from sections which have been cemented in the usual manner on the slide with albumin-glycerine or serum-glycerine. Transfer them from absolute alcohol into 96% alcohol (methyl alcohol) and then cover them with a few drops of the following solution:

Commercial collodion solution ....1 part by volume
Ether ....4 parts by volume
Methyl alcohol (or 96% pure ethyl alcohol,
   not isopropyl alcohol) ....4 parts by volume

Allow the greater part of the dilute collodion solution to run off the slide again, wait until a film begins to form over the sections, and place them immediately in 70% alcohol. Drying out of the sections must also be strictly avoided in this case. Obviously, objects which have been fixed in mercuric chloride must also be iodized in this method. The collodion film must not be deposited too thickly, since collodion is stained intensely with many stains. If the film is thin enough, a small degree of staining will not interfere.

Freezing Before Sectioning

The freezing method must be mentioned here as well. It has some importance in microtome technique as a rapid method and for special investigations. However, the importance of frozen sectioning in microtome technique is not as great as is usually supposed, since frozen sections are more difficult to treat than paraffin sections, and moreover do not usually show fine details as clearly. Use of the freezing method is justified in investigations which do not require much time, in fat preparations, and for impregnating nerve tissue.

In microtome technique, the objects are usually frozen with dry ice. Ethyl chloride is more suitable for your purposes; it is marketed in handy spray bottles. You can freeze fresh objects which are rich in water so hard with ethyl chloride that they can be sectioned easily.

Fasten a roughened metal plate on the table and place a slightly moistened (not dripping wet) piece of tissue paper on it. Place the object to be sectioned on the tissue paper. If the object is very small, embed it in a piece of raw potato.

Now open the closing lever on the ethyl chloride bottle very slightly and tilt the bottle in such a way that the liquid drips out. If you open the closing lever all the way, a thin jet of ethyl chloride will spray out. In the present situation, this would be undesirable.

Cover the object and the tissue paper with a few drops of ethyl chloride. Afterwards wait until the ethyl chloride has evaporated and then add a few more drops. Freeze the tissue paper and object in this way. Within a relatively short period of time it will become a solid block which in turn can be firmly frozen to the support.

Hold the straight razor with both hands, as for freehand sectioning of a paraffin block. In this case, however, do not press it through the object, but move the razor with a pulling motion, as in sectioning a fresh object which has not been embedded.

With some experience, very good results can be obtained with the freezing method.

In the preceding sections you have become acquainted with a few of the more complicated methods for preparing thin sections. However, it must again be emphasized strongly that in the majority of cases you can manage perfectly well with simple freehand sectioning of fresh and alcohol-hardened objects or objects embedded in paraffin. In the following chapters of this book the author intentionally has not described any investigation which could not be performed by the most primitive freehand-sectioning technique.

STAINING

The immense number of different types of staining methods for microscopic objects not only confuses many amateur microscopists, but experts also fall into the error of wanting to use a special staining method for each individual object and for each special structure. Actually you can manage with relatively few staining techniques once you understand that the goal of microscopic staining is not to make a preparation as gaudy as possible, but to get one in which contrasts are accentuated.

A very simple haematoxylin stain is often richer in contrast than a more or less blurred contrast stain involving three different stains.

It must be mentioned that a stained preparation under the microscope should be illuminated differently from an unstained one. In an unstained preparation, which is usually studied in a mounting medium with a low refractive index (such as water), you notice especially the differences in refraction of the individual structures. On the other hand, differences in coloration are examined in a stained preparation. Because of this, the unstained preparation is observed with the condenser diaphragm stopped down so that it is relatively narrow; the stained preparation is observed with the diaphragm opened relatively wide. For mounting a stained preparation it is proper to use a synthetic mounting medium with an index of refraction which is approximately equal to that of the mounted tissue (1.52–1.56) and is neutral. (See page 32.)

Generally Useful Stains

There are a few stains which can be used in like manner for both animal and plant objects. First of all, the various haematoxylin stains are easy to use and produce preparations which are stable and rich in contrast.

EHRLICH'S ACID HAEMATOXYLIN:

Haematoxylin...... 2 gm.
96% alcohol ......100 cc.

You can use isopropyl alcohol, but in no case methyl alcohol. Dissolve the haematoxylin and then add the following to the alcoholic haematoxylin solution:

Distilled water .... 100 cc.
Glycerine .... 100 c.c
Potassium alum .... 3 gm.
Glacial acetic acid ...... 10 cc.
Sodium iodate ($NaIO_3$) 0.4 gm.

Ehrlich's haematoxylin is one of the most reliable stain solutions. It stains nuclei an intense blue, the remaining structures bluish to grey shades. Transfer the objects from water into the solution for 2 to 10 minutes and then wash them off well with tap water. The time required for staining depends upon the kind of object to be stained and upon the age of the stain solution. It is important to wash the objects off especially carefully in tap water, since the stain contains a great deal of acid. Traces of acid which remain behind in the sections destroy the stain in the course of time. Change the wash water several times.

DELAFIELD'S HAEMATOXYLIN:

Haematoxylin......... 4 gm.
Absolute alcohol......25 cc.

To the alcoholic haematoxylin solution add:

Saturated aqueous solution of ammonia alum......400 cc.
(40 gm. ammonia alum in 400 cc. distilled water)
Sodium iodate ($NaIO_3$) .... 0.8 gm.
Glycerine ....100 cc.
Methyl alcohol...100 cc.

The solution must be filtered after a few days, and is ready for use. Delafield's haematoxylin is used a great deal and is better known than Ehrlich's haematoxylin. However, Ehrlich's haematoxylin is to be preferred, for in most cases it is cleaner and stains more clearly.

(Delafield's may also be ripened naturally by omitting the sodium iodate: According to Conn, add alcoholic solution of haematoxylin to the ammonia alum drop by drop and let stand exposed to air and light one week. Filter, then add 100 cc. glycerine and 100 cc. methyl alcohol. Let stand until the solution becomes dark, 4–5 hours. Filter and store in a tightly stoppered bottle for 6–8 weeks before using. Just before using, dilute with an equal volume of distilled water.)

If you stain in undiluted Delafield's haematoxylin solution, 3 to 6 minutes are usually long enough for staining. It is better to dilute the stain solution mentioned with a great deal of distilled water and to stain for a correspondingly longer period of time (several hours under some circumstances). Wash off the stain in tap water, whereupon you can see a change from red to blue.

HEIDENHAIN'S IRON HAEMATOXYLIN:

Heidenhain's haematoxylin shows the most varied constituents of tissue and cells. When using it, however, you must know precisely on which structures to place special value, so that these structures can be taken into account in differentation.

Mordant the sections for 3 to 12 hours in 1.5 to 4% iron alum solution. Then wash them with distilled water and place in the following haematoxylin solution:

Haematoxylin .... 0.5 gm.
96% alcohol.................. 10 cc.
Distilled water.............. 90 cc.
Sodium iodate ($NaIO_3$)... 0.1 gm.

The mordanted sections remain in this haematoxylin solution for at least 3 hours, and preferably 12 to 24 hours. They are then stained a deep black and display almost no structures at all when examined under the microscope. You must partially remove the stain from the sections again, i.e., differentiate them. Use a 2.5% iron alum solution (which has already been employed as a mordant) for this purpose. Place the sections in the iron alum solution, and soon they will give off thick clouds of stain. It requires some experience to discontinue differentiation at the right moment. If you differentiate too long, the cell constituents which were to be accentuated will be destained again; if you differentiate for too short a time, you will obtain dark, blurred images under the microscope. If examination under the microscope shows that the sections are differentiated to the proper extent, place them immediately in tap water which must be changed several times during a period of 15 to 30 minutes.

NAPHTHAZARIN: Naphthazarin, which is extremely easy to use and produces outstanding results, also belongs among the synthetic mordant stains which Becher introduced into microscope technique ("Becher stains").

Naphthazarin .... 0.25 gm.
Aluminium chloride ...... 5.0 gm.
Distilled water .... 100 cc.

Boil the solution for 5 minutes and filter it after cooling. It must be filtered again after a week. Transfer the sections from distilled water into the naphthazarin solution and stain them from an hour to a day. (The time required for staining differs greatly, depending upon the object and the age of the solution.) Since naphthazarin hardly overstains, it is better to stain somewhat too long than too short. Wash off the stain in distilled water. (Naphthazarin is a dye not to be confused with naphthalene or its derivatives. If it is difficult to obtain, you can use alizarin-cyanin RR instead.)

Staining Methods for Animal Tissue

Sections of animal tissue are very often stained with haemalum. However, according to the author's experience, haemalum does not always stain reliably. For this reason, Ehrlich's haematoxylin is almost always used in place of haemalum. Simple double stains with haematoxylin-eosin are very useful in animal histology. Stain the sections with Ehrlich's or Delafield's haematoxylin, as described above; wash off in tap water, rinse for a short time in distilled water, and stain with an 0.1% eosin solution. Haematoxylins stain primarily the nucleus, eosin chiefly the cytoplasmic structures.

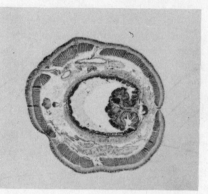

Illus. 1. Cross-section through an earthworm. The object which was embedded in paraffin was cut with a straight razor without a microtome (magnification about 30 ×). See Embedding (page 16) and Sectioning (page 18).

Beginners frequently make the mistake of staining too intensely with eosin so that blurred, indistinct images are obtained. Sections stained in eosin should only be tinted a light red. It is expedient to use erythrosin B in place of the usual eosin. Erythrosin B stains brighter, but otherwise corresponds to eosin in its staining action.

Transfer the sections from eosin into distilled water. They should remain in the water only until excess stain has been washed out, since eosin is extracted again very rapidly by water and solutions with low percentages of alcohol.

You can often stain smaller animals as specimens for general preparations and then mount them whole, i.e., unsectioned, as well. (For example: small worms, water fleas, and so forth.) Borax carmine (one of Grenacher's solutions) can be recommended especially for this purpose. Triturate

2.5 gm. of carmine with 4 gm. of borax, and dissolve the mixture in 100 cc. of boiling, distilled water. When the solution has cooled, add an additional 100 cc. of 70% alcohol and allow it to stand for a few days to a few weeks. Filter it before use.

Transfer the objects from 70% alcohol into the stain solution and let them remain in it until they have been stained all the way through. In some instances this will take a few days. After staining, differentiate them in hydrochloric acid and alcohol (100 cc. of 70% alcohol and 0.5 cc. of pure hydrochloric acid). Allow the objects to remain in the hydrochloric acid and alcohol, which must be changed several times in some cases. Again this can take hours or days. Finally, wash them off well in pure 70% alcohol.

Borax carmine stains practically nothing but the nuclei. Therefore, parts of tissue which are rich in nuclei appear darker in the total preparation than those which are poor in nuclei.

AZAN STAINING:

The azan stain developed by Heidenhain is rather tedious to carry out, but it produces such marvellous preparations that it must be mentioned here. There are a great many simplified modifications of azan staining, at least one of which will be described further on. However, none of the modifications even remotely approaches the quality of the original method. Azan staining shows collagenous connective tissue up to the finest fibrils in a bright blue and can consequently be classed among special staining methods for connective tissue. But in addition to this, all of the other tissue constituents, especially glandular tissue, are made to stand out so sharply that azan staining, even for general preparations, has not as yet been surpassed by any other method. A disadvantage of azan staining is that it gives good results only in very thin sections (less than 10μ thick). Consequently, anyone who does not have a microtome at his disposal can perform azan staining only on smear preparations (see p. 98).

You will need the following solutions for azan staining:

AZOCARMINE SOLUTION:

Azocarmine G ......   0.1 gm.
Distilled water ......100 cc.

Boil the suspension of azocarmine G in water for a short time and filter after cooling. Then add 1 cc. of glacial acetic acid to every 100 cc. of the filtrate.

ANILINE BLUE – ORANGE G – GLACIAL ACETIC ACID:
Water soluble aniline blue ...... 0.5 gm.
Orange G .... 2.0 gm.
Glacial acetic acid .... 8.0 cc.
Distilled water ....100 cc.

Heat the solution to boiling and filter after cooling. Before use, dilute it with about twice its volume of distilled water.

ALCOHOLIC ANILINE SOLUTION:
Aniline oil.................. 0.1 cc.
90% alcohol ....100 cc.

ACETIC ACID – ALCOHOL:
96% alcohol ....100 cc.
Glacial acetic acid ...... 1 cc.

5% AQUEOUS SOLUTION OF PHOSPHOTUNGSTIC ACID.

First place the sections in alcoholic aniline and transfer them from this into a solution of azocarmine heated to 55–60° C. If you have an incubator at your disposal, stain in the incubator. If you do not, you have to keep the stain solution at about 50° C. for the time required for staining —about 30 to 60 minutes.

After staining with azocarmine, rinse for a short time in distilled water and differentiate in the alcoholic aniline solution until you can see the nuclei clearly under the microscope. Interrupt the differentation by placing the sections in acetic acid-alcohol. Wash off the acetic acid-alcohol in distilled water and place the sections in 5% phosphotungstic acid solution for mordanting. Leave them in this solution for about 30 minutes to 3 hours. Next rinse them off with distilled water for a short time and stain for P to 1 hour in aniline blue – orange G – glacial acetic acid solution. It is best to transfer them from this stain solution without further washing in distilled water into 96% alcohol. Differentiate them there until the tissue constituents stand out sharply and are no longer overstained. Transfer them next to isopropyl alcohol which you should change at least once.

A successful azan stain shows connective tissue to be stained blue, the nuclei red, muscle tissue reddish or bluish, and other tissue in various tones.

In a few useful modifications of azan staining an attempt has been made to replace azocarmine with nuclear fast red.[3]

---

[3] Domagh, Zach, and Geidies; the latter quoted from a private communication to the author.

You will need the following solutions for a nuclear fast red-aniline blue-orange G stain which is easy to carry out.

NUCLEAR FAST RED – ALUMINIUM SULPHATE SOLUTION:
Heat 100 cc. of a 5% aqueous solution of aluminium sulphate almost to the boiling point. Dissolve 0.1 gm. of nuclear fast red (rare but obtainable) in the hot solution and filter after cooling.

5% PHOSPHOTUNGSTIC ACID SOLUTION.

ANILINE BLUE – ORANGE G – GLACIAL ACETIC ACID SOLUTION.
(See above for preparation.)

Transfer the sections from distilled water into the nuclear fast red solution. They should be stained in this until the nuclei are an intense red ($\frac{1}{2}$ to 2 hours). After rinsing in distilled water, place the sections in phosphotungstic acid for 10 minutes, rinse them off for a short time with water, and transfer into the aniline blue-orange G solution for $\frac{1}{2}$ to 1 hour. Differentiate them in 96% alcohol and dehydrate in absolute isopropyl alcohol. The staining effect resembles real azan staining, but the tones are duller and very fine structures do not emerge so clearly.

If nuclear fast red is not obtainable, use the original Mallory stain:
0.1% AQUEOUS SOLUTION OF ACID FUCHSINE
1.0% AQUEOUS SOLUTION OF PHOSPHOMOLYBDIC ACID

ANILINE BLUE – ORANGE G – OXALIC ACID SOLUTION:
Aniline blue ...... 0.5 gm.
Orange G .... 2.0 gm.
Oxalic acid ...... 2.0 gm.
Distilled water ...100 cc.

Boil, allow to cool, and filter the solution.
Stain in the acid fuchsine, rinse in distilled water, and put the sections in the phosphomolybdic acid for 3–5 minutes. Rinse in distilled water and stain in aniline blue – orange G – oxalic solution for 2 minutes. Rinse in distilled water and differentiate in 96% alcohol. Transfer through absolute alcohol and xylene and mount in a synthetic resin.

Staining Methods for Plant Tissues

Almost all plant tissues can be stained reliably and neatly with haematoxylin. Delafield's haematoxylin is especially recommended for plant sections; Ehrlich's also usually gives good results.

CHLORAZOL BLACK E (*Colour Index:* Direct Black 38) is a very outstanding stain which is easy to use. Prepare a saturated solution of the stain in

27

Illus. 2. Film impression of the underside of a leaf from stinging nettle, Urtica (magnification 440×; photo by M. Deckart).

See Film Impression Techniques (page 38).

70% ethyl or isopropyl alcohol and stain for 5 to 20 minutes depending upon the thickness of the sections (the thicker the section, the shorter the staining time). Wash the stain off in 80—90% alcohol. Chlorazol black E stains in shades ranging from black through dark grey and dark green to light grey. Nonlignified cell walls are usually shown as pure black. It is possible to combine chlorazol black staining with stains used expressly for wood such as safranine or chrysoidine. For procedures with fungi, see page 218.

The objects are treated differently, depending upon whether you want to study the structure of a plant organ from the various tissues (plant anatomy) or to examine the constituents of individual cells (nucleus, cytoplasmic structures, and so forth: cytology). Proper fixing is indispensable for cytological studies. Bouin's and Romeis' fixing mixtures as well as Heidenhain's susa can be especially recommended for this purpose. Heidenhain's iron haematoxylin should be considered first of all for staining cytological studies. With proper differentation you can show almost all of the known cytoplasmic structures with the aid of this stain (but obviously not in one and the same section).

Studies of plant anatomy can usually be performed even on objects which are not so well fixed. Ordinarily, alcohol is satisfactory for fixing. Since the cell content plays no role in studies of plant anatomy, it is removed with Javelle water (a bleach). Even relatively thick sections then produce clear and lucid images under the microscope. Transfer sections from water into Javelle water for 15 to 45 minutes, depending upon the thickness of the sections. When the cell contents have been completely dissolved (wash off sections for a short time in water and check them under the microscope), place the sections in acidified water (a few drops of glacial acetic acid in 50 cc. of water—several minutes). Wash off in one or two changes of distilled water and then stain. Sections which have beem cemented with albumin-glycerine cannot be treated with Javelle water.

TRIPLE STAIN WOOD-CELLULOSE-CORK (cutin) of F. Buxbaum[4] is one of the best multiple stains for plant objects. It is not only suitable for elucidating purely anatomical problems, but shows the cell walls effectively and also accentuates the cytoplasmic constituents nicely.

Dilute freshly filtered Delafield's haematoxylin with distilled water so that the solution becomes a light wine red. Then add enough chrysoidine Y-solution in distilled water (which has also been freshly filtered) so that the mixture has a yellowish tinge. The mixture is not stable and

---

[4] *Mikrokosmos* (Franckh'sche Verlagshandlung, Stuttgart), *41* (1952), 264.

must be freshly prepared before each staining. The staining process must be checked several times under the microscope so that the haematoxylin does not overstain. After staining, the sections are blued in tap water. Carry out dehydration in a series of solutions containing increasing percentages of alcohol.

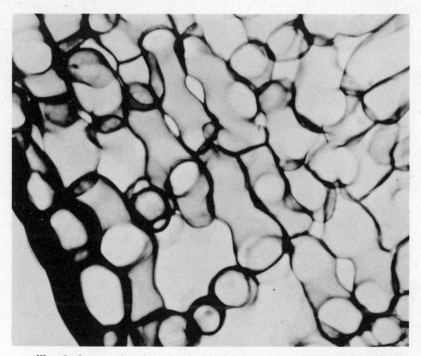

Illus. 3. Cross-section through a leaf of Helleborus niger. Thicker free-hand section stained with the PAS reaction according to the method of Hotchkiss and McManus (magnification about 400×). See PAS reaction (page 43).

Add some chrysoidine to the individual alcohol solutions to stain the wood more intensely. Transfer the sections from absolute alcohol into xylene, to which enough of a freshly filtered solution of Sudan III in xylene has been added so that it looks bright red. If examination under the microscope shows intensive red staining of the cork tissue and the cuticle, rinse off in pure xylene and mount in a synthetic mounting medium. Cellulose is stained violet, cork and cutin red, and wood yellow.

ECKERT'S FUCHSINE-ANILINE BLUE stain is very simple: Stain for about 10 minutes in a 1% solution of basic fuchsine (rosanaline-hydrochloride) in distilled water. After rinsing for a short time in distilled water, sections are transferred from the fuchsine solution into a 1% aqueous solution of aniline blue to which 1 cc. of glacial acetic acid had been added to each 100 cc. The fuchsine is extracted from the sections of the aniline blue solution, indeed more rapidly from the nonlignified cell walls than from the lignified ones. Differentiate in the aniline blue solution until only the lignified elements (e.g., bundles of vessels) are still stained red, and then differentiate the aniline blue stain in its turn in 90% alcohol (methyl alcohol). Finally, transfer into absolute isopropyl alcohol which is changed twice.

Successful preparations show lignified membranes to be a bright red, nonlignified ones blue.

Pararosaniline may be used in the Eckert stain. If this is done, alter the formula as follows: Suspend 1 gm. of pararosaniline in 100 cc. of distilled water. Add hydrochloric acid to the suspension drop by drop, shaking steadily while adding, until all the dye particles are completely dissolved. Then proceed as outlined above.

GENTIAN VIOLET (crystal violet) staining is distinguished by simple manipulation and universal applicability. (Actually, according to Conn, the name gentian no longer labels a certified stain. Users should specify crystal violet for bacteriological and histological work where a deep blue-violet is required; but should order methyl violet 2B for histological procedures where a reddish shade is called for.) Since gentian violet is extracted very rapidly in the alcohol series, it is expedient to stain in an alcoholic solution. Prepare a saturated solution of the stain in 70% alcohol. For staining, dilute this stock solution with 70% alcohol. It is more or less a matter of taste how highly you choose to dilute it. Naturally you must stain for a longer time in very dilute solutions, and only a short time in more concentrated ones.

Differentiate sections stained with gentian violet in 96% alcohol and then transfer them immediately into terpineol, which should be changed twice.

The double stain, HAEMATOXYLIN-SAFRANINE, is very often used to separate lignified and nonlignified tissues (woody and nonwoody) in plant sections. The procedure given here is very safe and gives satisfactory results. A great many other formulae exist.

Stain with Delafield's haematoxylin, wash off in tap water, and place the sections in a solution of 2 gm. of safranine in 100 cc. of 50% alcohol. (Do not use methyl alcohol.) You will obtain the best results if you stain

do not, in any case, dry out. This can happen easily when you press them with cotton. The method is especially suitable for paraffin sections which have been cemented with albumin or serum-glycerine, but can also be used for thin freehand sections which are not wavy.

You can get around the absolute alcohol and xylene with the aid of terpineol. Terpineol (not to be confused with oil of turpentine!) is soluble in 90% alcohol, xylene, and certain synthetic mounting media. Because of this, you can transfer the sections from 90% alcohol into terpineol, which absorbs the remaining traces of water, and mount them directly in the mounting medium—after a second passage through terpineol if necessary.

The use of the ethyl ether of ethylene glycol (ethyl cellosolve) has already been mentioned above for dehydration. You can transfer the sections from water or alcohol into ethyl cellosolve and from here place them directly in xylene. Dehydration in ethyl cellosolve requires 5 to 15 minutes, depending upon the thickness of the sections. Consequently, using ethyl cellosolve saves considerable time, for which you can certainly put up with the relatively high price, especially since you will usually need only small quantities.

Beginners try again and again to carry out dehydration simply by allowing the sections to dry out. This method will always lead to ugly, shrunken preparations in which the finer details can no longer be recognized. You should therefore note: a section should never dry out under any circumstances—no matter from which liquid it might come.

Mounting in Water-Soluble Media

Mounting in water-soluble media has always been a problem child for the microscopist. That is, many objects do not withstand very well the complete dehydration which is necessary for mounting in resins. Besides, you can save considerable time by using a water-soluble mounting medium, for the tedious process of dehydration can be omitted entirely or in part. Unfortunately, however, all of the well-known mounting media which are suitable for objects containing water are less suitable or even completely unsuitable for stained preparations. Besides, preparations mounted in resins are much more stable than preparations produced with glycerine or glycerine jelly—the most widely used water-containing mounting media.

GLYCERINE JELLY AND GLYCERINE AS MOUNTING MEDIA

It is advisable to buy glycerine jelly ready-made. First transfer the sections from water into a graded series of glycerine-water solutions (e.g., glycerine-water—1:3; 2:3; 1:1) and then mount in glycerine jelly. Complicated equipment has been devised to liquefy glycerine jelly. It is superfluous. Take a lump of solid glycerine jelly of suitable size from the stock bottle, warm it on a microscope slide until it begins to melt, place the sections in it, and cover with a cover-glass. Repeated liquefaction of jelly should by all means be avoided, for it will become crumbly.

After the glycerine jelly has solidified, the preparation must still be provided with a lacquer ring, since otherwise the jelly would dry out and develop cracks in the course of time. Remove all traces of jelly from around the cover-glass and draw a lacquer ring around the cover-glass with a camel's-hair brush. The lacquer ring must overlap the upper side of the cover-glass and join slide and cover-glass to one another without a gap, so that the preparation is really tightly sealed. After the first lacquer ring dries, it is advisable to apply a second one and, in some circumstances, even a third. It is advisable to use a sealing lacquer which is made especially for microscopic applications and can be obtained from suppliers in this field. Most of these lacquers can be diluted with acetone if they become too viscous. You can obtain especially fine lacquer rings by using a so-called lacquer-ring machine, which, however, can only be used for round cover-glasses. Suitable objects for mounting in glycerine jelly are, for example, wood sections and preparations of cereal grains and flour products, pollen grains, and others described in Chapter 2.

Glycerine is used as a mounting medium in the same way as glycerine jelly. However, since the lacquer ring is much more difficult to apply in glycerine preparations than in glycerine jelly preparations, in general glycerine jelly is preferred.

If you do not work with a lacquer-ring machine, the lacquer rings fit evenly only in rare cases. Moreover, quite often they are not airtight. Preparations which are not very tightly sealed deteriorate in the course of time. Zeller (see below) has now found a method which makes it possible to obtain glycerine and glycerine jelly preparations which are very definitely sealed. To be sure, the technique requires more skill than sealing with a lacquer ring, but absolutely guarantees neat preparations which are really permanent.

ZELLER'S METHOD: Place a drop of glycerine or glycerine jelly on a small cover-glass, put the object in it, and cover with a large cover-glass moved to the spot from above with a pointed pair of tweezers. The glycerine drop must be measured so that it just fills the space between the large and small cover-glasses. Glycerine drops should not ooze out under the small cover-glass. Now smear plenty of a thinly liquid mounting medium (diluted with xylene or benzene if necessary) on the slide so that it covers an area about as large as the large cover-glass. Now hold the large cover-glass carefully with the tweezers so that the small cover-glass sticks to the bottom. Place the large and small cover-glasses in the mounting medium which has been smeared on the slide (the small cover-glass first). The mounting medium immediately surrounds the small cover-glass and seals the drop of glycerine located between the large and small cover-glasses as tightly as possible with the embedded object.

POLYVINYL ALCOHOL AS A MOUNTING MEDIUM

In recent years many methods have been described for mounting with polyvinyl alcohol. The author has obtained very good results with the mounting medium of Gray and Wess which is described next. Because of the relatively low refractive index of this medium, even those structures of unstained preparations which are almost optically invisible in glycerine jelly can be seen sharply and distinctly. The mounting medium hardens so rapidly under the cover-glass that the slide can be placed vertically even after a few hours without fear that the cover-glass will get out of place. It is not absolutely necessary to seal preparations which are to be kept for many years with lacquer, but this should probably be recommended.

MOUNTING MEDIUM OF GRAY AND WESS:
    Polyvinyl alcohol ...... 2 gm.
    70% acetone............ 7 cc.
    Glycerine .... 5 cc.
    Lactic acid .... 5 cc.
    Water   ....10 cc.

First of all, triturate the dry, powdery alcohol into a paste with acetone. Then mix half of the water (5 cc.) with the glycerine and lactic acid and stir the mixture into a paste. Finally add the remaining 5 cc of water dropwise while stirring continuously. At first the substance is cloudy. It becomes translucent when you heat it in the water bath for about 10 minutes.

CONTAINERS FOR FIXING, DEHYDRATING, AND STAINING

Specimen bottles with flat bottoms and cork stoppers are universally used glass containers. For most purposes you will be able to manage with two sizes: 60×70 mm. and 43×50 mm.

For fixing, dehydrating, and staining free sections, make yourself a staining sieve in which the objects can be suspended in the various liquids. File off the closed end of a test tube with a glass file or an ampoule file, or simply crack it off after heating it properly. Squeeze out a few leaves of gelatine which have been softened in water and melt them in a water bath. Dip a layer of surgical gauze in the liquid gelatine (you can also use bone glue) and then cement the surgical gauze to the lower opening of the tube, which is now open at both ends. Gelatine which has remained behind in the meshes of the surgical gauze is removed by blowing it out before it can harden.

When the gelatine has hardened, place the tube in formalin for several hours. In this way the gelatine which is cemented to the glass along with the gauze will become insoluble in all of the solvents which will later be used. After you wash out the formalin thoroughly, the staining sieve is ready for use. Tie a thread around the neck of the sieve by means of which it can be suspended in the various liquids (Fig. 1). Anyone who wants to treat several objects at the same time can also make such a staining sieve with a larger glass tube.

Fig. 1. Staining sieve seen from the side and bottom.

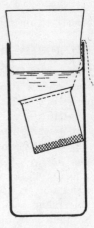

Fig. 2. Staining sieve suspended in a glass cylinder.

For fixing, fill a large specimen bottle with the fixative, place the object in the staining sieve and suspend the sieve in the liquid (Fig. 2). In this way the fixative can enter the object from all sides. For dehydrating, fill large specimen bottles with alcohol at different concentrations and suspend the object in the staining sieve. You will then see how the water or water-containing alcohol sinks to the bottom in streaks called schlieren. Sections can be treated in an analogous manner in a staining sieve during staining and dehydration.

Watch-glasses are indispensable aids for many purposes in microscopy. For example, you will use the small watch-glasses to stain and dehydrate individual sections, since you will then need only small amounts of the liquids in question.

The so-called salt-cellars are blocks of glass into which a hollow has been ground. They are used if the objects must remain lying in certain liquids (stains, etc.) for long periods of time.

Sections which have been cemented on a microscope slide are passed through the alcohol series and stained by placing the entire slide in the solutions under consideration. For this purpose you will obviously need larger containers. There are rectangular containers (called Coplin's jars) in which two of the inner sides are provided with grooves. You can place the slide between each set of two grooves and treat 12 or even more slides in one operation in this way. Other containers used for staining cemented sections are cylindrical in shape. If you place a set of two slides back to back, 6 microscope slides can be arranged in such a jar. The larger specimen bottles into which one slide fits, are also simplest (and least expensive) for this purpose.

FILM IMPRESSION TECHNIQUES AND GUMMED TAPE METHODS

The microscopist often finds himself posed with the problem of examining some surface structures. If he does not have a vertically illuminated microscope at his disposal, he can make use of a film impression. It is easiest to use an approximately 4% solution of collodion in ether and alcohol which can be obtained commercially for this purpose. An 8% collodion solution in equal volumes of ether and 96% ethyl alcohol is more suitable. A little of the collodion solution is dropped on the object (polished metal, wood, skin, surfaces of plant leaves, and others) and spread out on it. After the solvent has evaporated, a thin, translucent film remains behind which is carefully removed while blowing on it. The film then contains an impression of even the finest surface sculptures which can now be examined under the microscope. Anyone who has a phase contrast microscope can use it here to special advantage.

For obtaining an impression of textile fabrics Reumuth[6] uses the cement *Uhu hart*. (This is similar to the clear cellulose nitrate liquid filler—or

---

6 H. Reumuth, *Melliand Textilberichte, 36* (1955), 533–539. Also Th. Loske, *Mikrokosmos*, 48 (1959) 161–168.

"dope"—used in constructing model aircraft. It is also used by photographers as a backing for sensitive film.) He smears a slide with the glue or cement, waits until the cement has reached a suitable consistency by evaporation of the solvent, and then presses the fabric onto the coated side. The fabric is then pulled off with a jerk in the same way a doctor tears off adhesive tape. In the impression left you can see not only the structures of the fibres, but also faults in the fabric, signs of wear, sites of fracture, and so forth. The method requires some practice. Above all you must learn to wait for the right moment at which the cement is neither too fluid nor too hard.

The gummed tape method of Kisser and Lehnert[7] is related to the film impression technique. It serves for examining deposits of dust on plant leaves.

A technique which makes it possible to evaluate the distribution and amount of dusts produced by industrial plants is of immediate interest because of increasing air-pollution. Many of these dusts have a definite chemical composition. They present a characteristic image under the microscope; typical guiding elements form a basis on which you can determine even the origin of a given dust.

Small particles of dust adhere to plant leaves. You can prove their existence most conveniently there.

Gummed tape on a cellulose or plastic base, for example, "Scotch" tape, can serve for making impression preparations. Place the leaf on a hard smooth base, roll the gummed tape on it (taking care to avoid air currents) and press firmly so that even the particles of dirt which are located deeply come into contact with the gummy substance. Stick the gummed tape directly onto a microscope slide after removing the leaf. Start with one end and press the tape slowly and continuously onto the slide, again taking care to avoid air currents. In this way the distribution of the particles of dirt is itself retained. If the leaf is contaminated heavily with fine dust, the distribution of dust almost amounts to a pattern of the surface sculptures of the leaf.

CUTICULAR ANALYSIS

An extremely thin membrane covers the epidermis of the part of land plants which are above ground. This membrane is impervious to water and therefore protects plants from much too large losses of water through evaporation. It consists chiefly of a wax-like substance, cutin.

---

7 *Mikrokosmos, 47* (1958), 165–168.

The cuticle is extremely resistant; even strong acids cannot affect it. Consequently, it is even retained in fossilized remains of plants.

The structures of the cuticle differ in different species of plants. Because of this you can determine the species of a plant from tiny particles of the cuticle—provided only that you have sufficient material for comparison. Cuticular analysis (i.e., identifying a plant from the cuticle) is therefore used in palaeontology to examine residues from primitive plants. Even pulverized parts of plants can be diagnosed by this method. This is very useful for powdered drugs. And, finally, cuticular analysis can also be used in criminological techniques.

The cuticle duplicates all of the forms of its base, the epidermis, quite faithfully (contours of epidermal cells, stomata, hair structures, and so forth). These are the epicuticular structures. In addition, there are idio-cuticular structures, structures characteristic of the cuticle itself (granular or nodular protuberances, striations, the cuticular folds which can appear in a smaller or larger number, short or long, coarse or fine, and usually run in a quite definite direction). Cuticular structures from different parts of the same plant can differ from one another.

You must isolate the cuticle to examine it under the microscope. For this purpose, use chromic and nitric acids to dissolve all parts of the plant with the exception of the cuticle. Keep a stock solution of this macerating fluid on hand which is diluted before use (see below). For very thin cuticles, mix one volume of the stock solution and one volume of water; for thicker ones, two volumes of the stock solution and one volume of water. After 1 to 4 hours all parts of the plant will have been dissolved with the exception of the cuticles, which then float on the surface as extremely thin and soft, transparent membranes. Catch them with a microscope slide and transfer them into water to wash them off.

It is expedient to begin by examining the leaves of different plants. Cut out squares with edges about 1/2 cm. long and place them in the macerating fluid. Material which has been preserved in alcohol must first be washed off in water.

Stain the isolated cuticles with the fat stain, Sudan red III (see below), wash them off in water, and mount in glycerine jelly. If you do not want to make permanent preparations, you can examine them in a drop of zinc chloride-iodine solution.

Cuticular analysis offers a rewarding field of work even to the amateur microscopist. The basic requirement is a collection of comparative preparations. Naturally, the unknown cuticles to be examined must be placed in the same mounting medium as the comparative preparation.

CHROMIC AND NITRIC ACIDS: Hot, saturated solution of chromic acid in concentrated nitric acid. After cooling and settling, store in a flask with a ground-glass stopper.

SUDAN RED: Heat 70% alcohol in a water bath. (Caution: the fumes are inflammable.) Dissolve 0.2–0.3 gm. Sudan III in 100 cc. of the hot alcohol. Filter after cooling.

HISTOCHEMICAL METHODS

Histochemistry attempts to identify constituents of tissue of a given chemical composition in sections prepared for microscopy. The best known example of a histochemical reaction is the iodine reaction for starch. Starch granules are stained blue when iodine is added, and can therefore be distinguished from other cellular inclusion bodies which often look very much the same. Histochemical reactions are continually increasing in importance in science and technology.[8]

Here you will become acquainted with three histochemical techniques of practical importance: the identification of fatty substances (lipides), vitamin C, and carbohydrates.

Detection of Lipides

Certain stains dissolve especially well in lipides, i.e., substances which behave like fats. If you place a section in the alcoholic solution of such a stain, the stain passes over from the poorer solvent—alcohol—into the better solvent, which is the lipide contained in the section (if the section does contain lipides). After washing off excess stain, the lipides will appear stained for that reason.

NOTE: In Great Britain, the term lipide does not include the neutral fats, fatty acids, or sterols. It is restricted to compounds which, on hydrolysis, yield an alcohol or sugar, a base, and a fatty acid. In the United States, the term includes fatty acids and soaps, neutral fats, waxes, steroids, and phosphotides.

Sudan black B is an excellent fat stain. Cover 0.1 gm. of Sudan black with 100 cc. of 70% alcohol and heat in a water bath until it boils. (Caution: alcohol fumes are inflammable.) Filter the solution after it has cooled.

Naturally, the sections on which the determination of fat is to be performed should not first be treated with fat solvents. For this reason, alcohol-fixed material or even paraffin sections cannot be considered. Work with freehand or frozen sections of objects which have been fixed in formalin. (To try the technique, sections through oil-containing seeds

---

[8] Anyone who wants to examine them in more detail will find an excellent review in the compilation of W. Lipp: *Histochemische Methoden*, R. Oldenbourg-Verlag, Munich, a collection started in 1954.

are recommended, for example, hazelnuts or filberts, walnuts, or almonds.)

Fat droplets in the cells are stained blue-black after 10 to 20 minutes. Then rinse off the sections in distilled water and mount them in glycerine jelly. (Only mounting in water-soluble mounting media can be considered since Permount, for example, would extract the fats.)

It is advisable to contrast stain nuclei of zoological objects with nuclear fast red-aluminium sulphate (see p. 27).

Detection of Vitamin C

Vitamin C (ascorbic acid) is an essential agent for man which the body itself cannot produce (daily requirement about 50 mg.). The histochemical detection of vitamin C would be of great practical importance because of this alone, but it is also important for many studies of metabolism and physiology in plants and animals.

Only relatively few strong reducing agents can precipitate metallic silver from a highly acid solution of silver nitrate (in contrast to a neutral or alkaline silver nitrate solution, which is very easily reduced). Vitamin C is one of these reducing agents, and the histochemical test depends upon this. If you place sections in an acid silver nitrate solution, a fine-grained precipitate of metallic silver (which looks black) is formed at places in the cells which contain vitamin C.

Preparation of the ACID SILVER NITRATE SOLUTION: Dissolve 1 gm. silver nitrate in 20 cc. 1% acetic acid. The solution is stable in the dark for a long time if it is well-stoppered in brown bottles.

When working with parts of plants it is advisable to use unfixed freehand sections of fresh material and to place them immediately in the silver nitrate solution. Even after a few minutes (at most after 10 minutes), you can examine the sections in a drop of silver nitrate solution. In cells which previously contained vitamin C you will find black granules of metallic silver precipitated from the silver salt solution by vitamin C.

Metal instruments should not come into contact with the silver nitrate solution.

MAKING PERMANENT PREPARATIONS: Place the fresh sections for 10 minutes in the silver nitrate solution. Next wash them for 10 minutes in several changes of distilled water, treat for 10 minutes with 5% sodium thiosulphate solution, and wash off again for 10 minutes with several changes of distilled water. Contrast stain weakly with 0.1% eosin solution, dehydrate, and mount in a synthetic mounting medium after treating first with xylene or terpineol.

Animal organs are treated as whole mounts: place fresh slices of organs,

2 to 3 mm. in size, into the silver nitrate solution for 10 minutes. Wash off for 15 to 20 minutes in several changes of distilled water. Place in a 5% sodium thiosulphate solution for 10 minutes, and then in several changes of distilled water for 15 to 20 minutes. Treat with 96% alcohol, dehydrate, and embed in paraffin (see p. 16). Contrast stain the paraffin sections with nuclear fast red-aluminium sulphate.

For very accurate studies, the preparation should be carried out in the dark (dark-room with red light) up to dehydration. However, it is usually satisfactory to work in daylight.

Spruce needles, parsley leaves, or the green parts of a paprika seed are recommended for practicing the method. Among animal organs the adrenal cortex of mammals is especially rich in vitamin C.

A negative result in this reaction does not necessarily prove that vitamin C is absent.

Detection of Carbohydrates

Polysaccharides, such as starch, glycogen, cellulose, chitin, and many glycoproteins (proteins with sugar components) are a bright violet-red in the periodic acid-Schiff (PAS) reaction. By the action of periodic acid, aldehyde groups in these compounds are liberated; with these the Schiff reagent (fuchsine-sulphurous acid) forms a coloration complex.

The PAS reaction is also extremely well-suited to purely morphological studies of plant tissue, since it shows the cell walls bright and sharp as no other stain does. It is warmly recommended, especially for showing the coloration of parasitic fungi in plant tissues. According to Kligman, Mescon and DeLamater,[9] fungal hyphae can also be detected in an excellent manner with the aid of the PAS reaction. The somewhat simplified method of von Stosch,[10] which is satisfactory for most purposes will be given next. The technique was introduced by Hotchkiss[11] and McManus.[12]

The trickiest point in the method is preparing the Schiff's reagent. The instructions that are given here come from Graumann.[13]

---

[9] *American Journal of Clinical Pathology, 21* (1951), 86–91.

[10] *Zeitschrift für wissenschaftliche Mikroskopie und für mikroskopische Technik* (S. Hirzel Verlag, Stuttgart), *62* (1955), 305–310.

[11] *Archives of Biochemistry, 16* (1948), 131–141.

[12] *Stain Technology, 23* (1948), 99–108.

[13] *Zeitschrift für wissenschaftliche Mikroskopie und für mikroskopische Technik 61* (1953), 225.

1. Schiff's reagent: Dissolve 0.5 gm. standard pararosaniline (parafuchsine), acridine-free, completely in 15 cc. of 1 N hydrochloric acid without heating by shaking. Dissolve 0.5 gm. potassium metabisulphite in 85 cc. distilled water and add.

The solution which is a bright red at first gradually becomes lighter and turns yellowish. After 24 hours shake the solution with 0.3 gm. of activated charcoal for 2 minutes and then filter.

It is important that the finished solution be almost clear or, at most, a light yellow. Reddish solutions cannot be used. You can recognize deteriorated solutions by the fact that they turn red. Schiff's reagent is stable for a long time, if it is kept well stoppered in brown bottles in the dark.

2. 1% aqueous solution of sodium metaperiodate.

3. Rinse containing SO_2: 200 cc. tap water $+10$ cc. of a 10% solution of potassium metabisulphite $+$ 10 cc. of 1 N hydrochloric acid. Prepare the mixture fresh each time before using it. You can keep the 10% solution of potassium metabisulphite in stock.

Place the objects, which have been fixed any way you like, in 96% alcohol (perhaps upwards through the alcohol series) for at least 24 hours. Transfer the sections from distilled water into the sodium periodate solution for 30 minutes, rinse off thoroughly with distilled water, and place them in Schiff's reagent. (Stopper or close the container.)

Plant sections with cell walls which are stained very intensely must be observed under the microscope at intervals of a few minutes. Carbohydrates, i.e., the plant cell walls, are gradually stained red. In thick sections the danger of overstaining exists. When the stain has become thick enough, stop the reaction by washing in the rinse which contains SO_2. Thin sections (microtome sections as thick as 30μ) and sections which only contain small amounts of carbohydrates (animal organs) can remain in Schiff's reagent for $\frac{1}{2}$ to 1 hour. Transfer the sections directly from Schiff's reagent into the rinse containing SO_2, and change the solution 3 times every 5 minutes. Finally wash out the sections thoroughly for 5 to 10 minutes in running tap water or tap water which has been changed several times. It is possible to contrast stain lightly with a 0.1% solution of light green or—preferably—Fast green FCF. Dehydrate and mount in a synthetic mounting medium.

In morphological studies of plants, starch granules in the cells which have been stained especially intensely, often interfere. According to von Stosch, the starch can be removed (digested) by placing it for 2 hours in a 2% solution of amylase. However, the objects should not be fixed with agents containing chromic acid in this case. (Amylase is supplied by Merck, for example.)

For studies of plant anatomy, in which you are only interested in the cell walls, remove the cell contents before the reaction with Javelle water. (Afterwards wash thoroughly with acidulated water, with distilled water, transfer into sodium metaperiodate, etc.) Then you will obtain preparations of almost unbelievable transparency with punctured, brightly stained cell walls.

If it is a question of distinguishing carbohydrates from all other chemical substances, a control experiment is necessary. Subject a section of the object to be examined to the entire procedure, but omit the treatment with sodium metaperiodate solution. This section must remain completely unstained. If it does show staining, the solutions should be checked. If the object is not treated first with alcohol, a reaction can occur with Schiff's reagent which is not due to carbohydrates.

2. Examining Foodstuffs

GRAINS AND GRAIN PRODUCTS

The problem here is to determine the composition of flour and baked goods and, if necessary, to establish the presence of adulterants and additives. Kernels of grain are particularly rich in starch, one of the most important materials stored by plants; plants store starch in the seeds of grain to nourish the embryos. If you rub a trace of flour in a drop of water on a microscope slide and examine it under the microscope, you will see that flour consists almost entirely of starch granules. Thus, starch is not only an important material stored by plants for their own use, it is also an important constituent of our human food.

The shape of individual starch granules varies considerably, depending upon the species of the plant. For this reason, the plant from which the starch granules originate can be identified in many cases by the shape of the starch granules alone (Fig. 3). Although it is necessary to know the form of the starch granules in question when examining foodstuffs, just remember that once in a while two different species of plants can have similar starch granules. In addition, baking the flour changes starch so much that you can hardly expect unequivocable results based merely on examination of the starch alone. Then too, you can always find isolated fragments of pericarps (fruit coats) and, in certain cases, even chaff. This tissue debris makes a positive identification possible in any case—if you are familiar with the structure of various seed kernels. Therefore, you must first become acquainted with the microscopic structure of the more important grains—a very exciting task which is not at all difficult.

Procure the grains described here and let them swell in water for several hours, which will allow you to cut them very easily. If you cannot treat the swollen kernels immediately, put them in a solution of equal volumes of methyl alcohol and glycerine. This solution preserves them without making them harder to cut. Cut them between small discs of cork or elderberry pith with a razor blade, examine them in water or, in the case of thick sections and opaque structures, in glycerine. (See p. 13 for details about microscopic technique.) Make permanent glycerine or glycerine jelly preparations of the best sections immediately, and in the

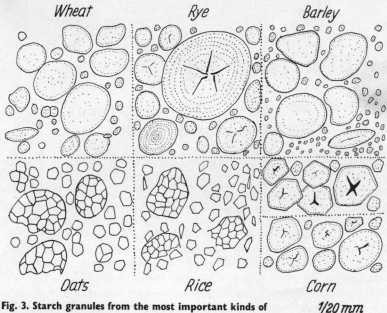

Fig. 3. Starch granules from the most important kinds of cereals. In corn (maize), the starch granules on top are from the horny endosperm; those on the bottom are from the floury endosperm.

1/20 mm

course of time you will have a valuable collection of comparative preparations. In this way you will be able to get along without staining in most cases. It is hardly worthwhile to make permanent preparations from starch granules since fresh material for comparison is, of course, always available in this case.

WHEAT

Even with relatively low-power magnification, a thin cross-section of a grain of wheat will reveal an image under the microscope like that shown in Fig. 4. First of all you will find the tissue of the pericarp. The topmost layer of the pericarp consists of cells which, as you will see, run longitudinally on the kernel; these are the longitudinal cells. After a few rows of longitudinal cells come the cross cells (Q) which run perpendicularly to the longitudinal cells. Both top layers are important in identification. Delicate tube-cells, which extend longitudinally along the kernel, follow inside the cross cells. The very thin seed coat (S), a vestige of tissue from the ovular integument, and finally the endosperm (the actual nutrient tissue) are attached to the pericarp.

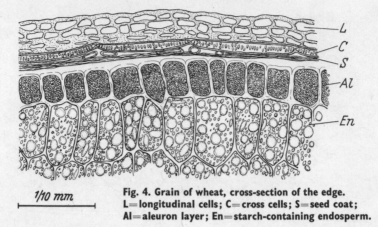

Fig. 4. Grain of wheat, cross-section of the edge.
L=longitudinal cells; C=cross cells; S=seed coat;
Al=aleuron layer; En=starch-containing endosperm.

1/10 mm

You will immediately notice two completely different cell forms in the endosperm. On the outside is a layer of cells with relatively thick walls and innumerable small, spherical inclusion bodies: these are solid protein spheres, called aleurone grains. The cells that contain them are called aleurone cells. Starch cells, which are large, thin-walled, and crammed full of starch granules, are attached to the inner side of the aleurone cells. Many starch granules will have been washed out in your preparation and will lie scattered individually around the section. You can now become more closely acquainted with wheat starch by means of these loose granules of starch (Fig. 3).

You will find both quite large and very small granules of starch. Large starch granules usually appear to be disc-shaped, or, when seen from the side, long and oval. Only rarely do the large granules of wheat starch display internal cavities—an important characteristic distinguishing them from rye starch. You can find rings in individual starch granules only in isolated cases.

Now place your cross-section in a drop of Lugol's solution (a solution of iodine and potassium iodide, see page 8) or in an alkaline iodine solution and place a cover-glass on top. Within a short time you will see that the starch granules have been stained blue to blue-black, but that the aleurone grains turn yellow-brown.

As has already been mentioned, debris from the pericarp is often a determining factor for the practical examination of flours and baked goods. In such fragments you will naturally see cell groups which are essential for identification—not in cross-section, but in a surface view. Consequently, you must be well acquainted with the surface view. Make very thin sections of the pericarp in which you will be able to see the

48

longitudinal and cross cells in particular. Place the sections on a slide in a drop of water so that first the upper surface will be turned toward the objective and then the lower surface.

In the surface view the longitudinal cells are thick-walled, distinctly pitted, elongated cells. Small points in thickened cell walls which have remained unthickened are called pits. They replace the thickening layers in the form of depressions, or even as long canals, and are contained by the original cell membrane which has remained unthickened—the pit membrane. Pits can be seen clearly in Fig. 5. They serve the living cells by facilitating the interchange of material.

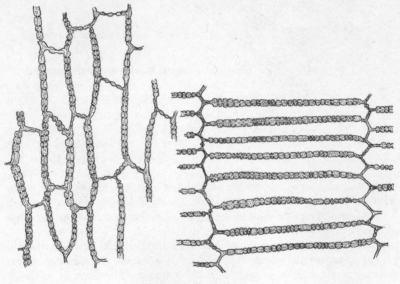

Fig. 5. Grain of wheat.
Longitudinal cells (left)
and cross cells (right).

There are unicellular hairs at the upper end of a grain of wheat which are so typical in their structure that they represent another characteristic. Cut off a few of these hairs together with their epidermis with a razor blade and examine them in water. You will see long cells with extremely thick walls. From about the middle of the hair to the tip, the cell walls are even thicker than the lumen (cell cavity). The base of the wheat hair, which appears to be distended, has blunt edges and is heavily pitted (Fig. 6).

49

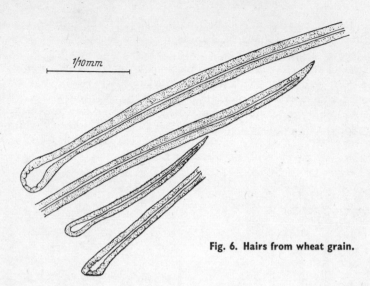

1/10mm

Fig. 6. Hairs from wheat grain.

RYE

You will first want to become acquainted with the image of the cross-section of rye, as you did with that of wheat. You will find that kernels of wheat and rye in cross-section can be distinguished from one another only with difficulty.

Examination shows very large and very small starch granules; but in rye—in contrast to wheat—all of the imaginable transitional stages between small and large granules are present. The interior of large granules of rye starch often reveals a branched cleft which is frequently star-shaped (hilum) and usually appears to be dark because of the air contained inside. You will quite often see thin, concentric rings in the starch granules of rye—especially in dim illumination. Starch granules of rye thus have a few characteristics which make it possible to distinguish between wheat and rye starch. However, the differences are not so great that observation of starch granules alone is sufficient when you examine flour. Consequently, you must look for still other distinguishing characteristics which will be found in the structure of the longitudinal and cross cells. (See Fig. 7.)

In surface views, the longitudinal cells of rye have thin walls which are beaded and not distinctly pitted. The end walls of cross cells in rye are arranged in rows like those of wheat, but they are rounded off instead of sloping to a point; and they are greatly thickened and not pitted. The long walls of cross cells are thin and beaded just as the longitudinal cells are.

The hairs of rye are longer than those of wheat. The wall of the rye hair is quite thin. In most cases the wall is considerably thinner than the lumen. The base of the hair appears to be only slightly distended, is rounded and only rarely pitted (Fig. 8).

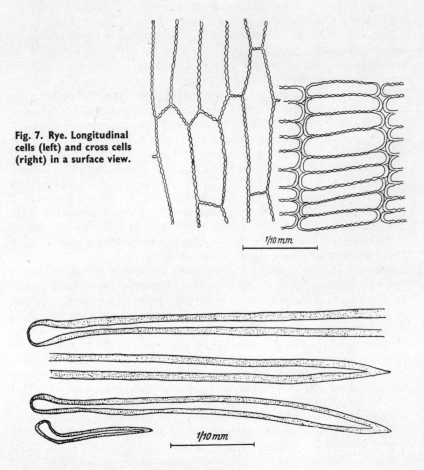

Fig. 7. Rye. Longitudinal cells (left) and cross cells (right) in a surface view.

1/10 mm

1/10 mm

Fig. 8. Hairs from the rye grain.

51

BARLEY

In addition to its pericarp and seed coat, the barley grain is covered by chaff. Consequently, you should consider the microscopic structure of the chaff closely, for it is just this which helps distinguish barley from other kinds of grain.

Make a cross-section through the chaff, pericarp and seed coat, and through the outer portions of the endosperm. Even at the first glance into the microscope you will see that the cross-sectional image of a barley grain differs basically from that of a grain of rye or wheat (Fig. 9).

You will find that the epidermis (the epiderm or outermost layer) of the chaff consists of thick cells which are irregular in shape. Under the epidermis you will see several layers of cells which are also thick and which appear to be more or less round in cross-section. This layer is called the hypoderm, and its cells are called hypodermal fibres. Later, in a surface view, you will be able to recognize the hypodermal fibres better. The following layer inside of the hypoderm is a spongy parenchyma, i.e., a spongy tissue of undifferentiated cells with many large intercellular spaces. (Intercellular spaces are air spaces passing through the tissue of plants in the form of fissures, small canals or even in the form of large cavities. They are often formed by the disintegration of the central lamellae at the edges of adjacent cells and the consequent recession of the cell walls. The plant body is traversed by a whole network of such intercellular spaces.)

The inner epidermis of the chaff is attached to the spongy parenchyma. You cannot usually see it clearly in cross-section.

You will find the pericarp and seed coat between the chaff and endosperm of barley. The pericarp is much more delicate in structure than in grains of wheat and rye, but the strong chaff takes over the function of protecting the seed kernel. In spite of this, you will see the same structural elements in the pericarp with which you have already become familiar in wheat and rye: longitudinal and cross cells, as well as tube cells, the latter being hard to find.

The seed coat exhibits no noteworthy details. However, in contrast to wheat and rye, the aleurone layer consists of several layers of cells. You will frequently find three layers of aleurone cells—a very important characteristic of barley, which can often be identified even in a surface view by focusing on different planes.

In order to have a complete picture of the structure of a barley grain and to be able to identify the components of barley in milled products unequivocally later on, you must now make surface sections through the

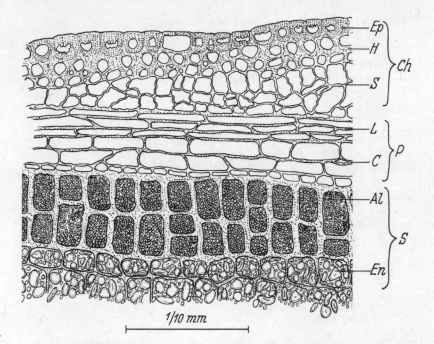

Fig. 9. Cross-section through the chaff and edge of a grain of barley. Ch=chaff; Ep=outer epidermis; H=hypoderm; S=spongy parenchyma; P=pericarp; L=longitudinal cells; C=cross cells; S=seed; Al=aleuron layer; En=starch-containing endosperm.

chaff and pericarp. You can easily make sections through the chaff on grain which has been softened. However, you will have to remove the chaff without damaging the pericarp in order to obtain good surface sections through the pericarp. It is best to remove the chaff after the grain has first been boiled for a short time in water.

In the surface view through the chaff you will first notice that the cells of the outer epidermis look completely different from the top as compared to cross-section. You will see tissue in which the cells are arranged in rows. In each of these rows of cells, very long cells alternate with very short ones (Fig. 10). The walls of the long cells, which are rather thick, are coiled in a characteristic manner so that the individual coils are tight. The short cells are usually located next to one another in pairs. The small cell is half surrounded by a slightly larger cell. Occasionally the smaller of the two short cells is drawn out into a hair. Somewhat larger short

53

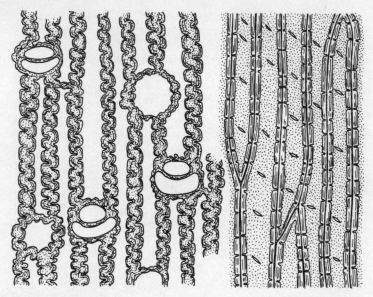

Fig. 10. Surface view of the epidermis (left) and the hypoderm (right) of barley chaff.

cells occurring separately and having slightly coiled walls are even rarer, but can still always be found.

Often the same surface view in which you can see the outermost epiderm of the barley chaff will also show the hypodermal fibres lying beneath the epidermis. You will see elongated, fibrous cells with oblique, cleft-like pits (Fig. 10).

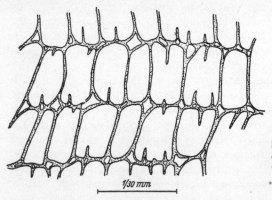

1/30 mm

Fig. 11. Spongy parenchyma of barley chaff, surface view.

In a surface section of the barley chaff you will see that the cell walls in the spongy parenchyma are very plicated (folded) so that the folds project rather deeply into the cell cavity (Fig. 11).

Longitudinal cells of the pericarp have thin walls and are only slightly pitted. You will often find large intercellular spaces on the short sides of cross cells.

Just as in wheat and rye, you will find rather large and very small starch granules in barley. The large granules have rather irregular contours; at isolated points they often appear to be distended, shaved off at the corners or swollen. Grains which are lenticular (bean-shaped) also occur (Fig. 3).

OATS

Like grains of barley, oat kernels have a chaff. In contrast to barley, the chaff is easy to remove from oats. Because of this, you will only rarely encounter constituents of the chaff in examining milled products. The characteristic starch granules and hairs are more important for identification of oats.

Remove the chaff from an oat grain, cut it and, using your knife, scrape a little material from the cut surface onto a slide. Even at low-power magnification you will see a large number of small granules—starch, as you can easily establish with the aid of the iodine reaction. However, these granules do not completely correspond to those which you already know: wheat, rye, and barley. If you examine the preparation in somewhat more detail, you will also find large starch granules which are composed of nothing but small individual granules (Fig. 3). Oat starch consists of nothing but such aggregates of small individual starch granules. In oats, it is not the individual granules which correspond to the starch granules of other plants, but rather the aggregates. You have probably damaged a large part of the starch granules by scraping, so that the granular aggregates have fallen apart into their individual granules—a process which also occurs regularly when oat grains are milled. Consequently, you will find primarily individual granules in oat meal.

The aggregated starch granules of oats are spherical or oval with smooth contours. The individual granules are polygonal and usually have blunt corners (Fig. 3). Oat starch can easily be confused with rice starch. Therefore, in some instances you must consult comparative preparations.

To obtain good sections through the hard and brittle oat chaff, you will have to soften the grain in a suitable manner. Place several grains from which the chaff is to be removed in a solution of equal volumes of methyl alcohol, glycerine and distilled water for a day or more. Then place them in this solution on a water bath which has been heated to a temperature slightly below the boiling point. Wait until the solution has been evaporated to approximately ⅓ of its original volume. After this preliminary treatment, which is also suitable for other hard objects, the chaff can be cut without great difficulty.

The oat chaff is similar in structure to that of barley. Therefore, you must look carefully so that you will notice the small differences. Surface views show an outer epiderm consisting of long and short cells. The long cells are closely coiled, but the coils are more helical (spiralling) than sinuous (Fig. 12). In oats, the hypoderm consists of fibrous cells much thicker and longer than those from barley chaff (Fig. 12). The following layer in oats, the spongy parenchyma, also located inside of the hypoderm, is made up of cells which are curved in at so many places that they appear

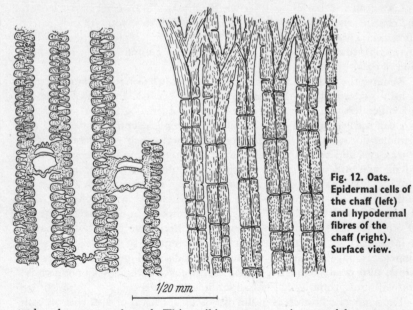

Fig. 12. Oats. Epidermal cells of the chaff (left) and hypodermal fibres of the chaff (right). Surface view.

1/20 mm

to be almost star-shaped. This striking structure is caused by numerous round intercellular spaces. In the spongy parenchyma of an oat grain you will look in vain for the projecting folds of the wall in the interior of the cell such as you saw in barley (Fig. 13). The inner epidermis of the chaff consists of oval cells with walls which are closely coiled. Everywhere on the inner epidermis you will find the stomata. (A stoma is understood to be a cleft-like opening between two adjacent cells, often bean-shaped, which leads into the system of intercellular spaces in the plant. In living

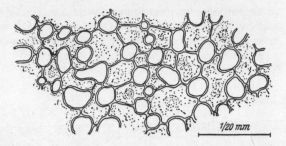

Fig. 13. Oats. Spongy parenchyma of the chaff. Surface view.

1/20 mm

tissue, the cleft can be opened or closed as needed by the two cells, the so-called guard cells. Stomata occur only in epidermal tissue, and can be seen particularly well on the lower epidermis of leaves.)

The longitudinal cells of the pericarp and the hairs attached to them are especially important in examining milled products. Surface views will usually show clearly the longitudinal cells. They are elongated with thin walls, slightly pitted (Fig. 14). In many places the exceedingly long hairs

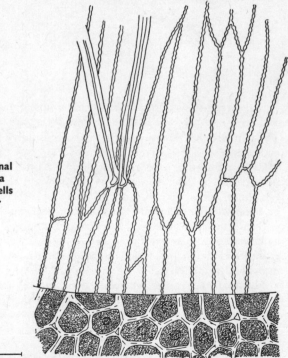

Fig. 14. Oats. Longitudinal cells of the pericarp in a surface view. Aleuron cells can be seen lying under them in the drawing.

1/10 mm

of the oat kernel project from longitudinal cells. You will see that the cell walls of the hairs are thick. Careful examination will show you that, strangely enough, the hairs are thickest in the middle, while the base of each hair is relatively narrow (Fig. 15).

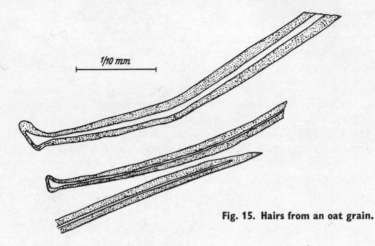

1/10 mm

Fig. 15. Hairs from an oat grain.

RICE

Hulls are removed from grains of rice during processing. The pericarp and seed coat, as well as the aleurone layer, are removed by polishing. Thus, in rice that you buy on the market, usually only the starch-bearing endosperm will be available for examination.

Cut a softened grain of rice and scrape a little endosperm from the cut surface into a drop of water. When you do this, take care that the "scraping" does not become too fine, for otherwise all of the starch granules will fall apart into their component granules.

Even during a superficial examination you will find that rice starch looks very much like oat starch. As in oats, you will find highly aggregated granules of starch which, for the most part, have fallen apart into their individual granules.

The aggregated starch granules of rice are irregularly formed; that is, they are not spherical or oval, as those of oats. The individual granules of rice starch are smaller than those of oats, and display sharp, pointed corners, as compared to oat starch in which the individual granules definitely have blunt corners (Fig. 3).

In rice flour, but to a greater degree in rice powder, you will hardly be able to find undamaged aggregated starch granules. Therefore, in order to examine them, you must consider the individual granules above all, and in a doubtful case make comparative preparations from oat starch.

CORN (Maize)

A cross-section through the edge of a grain of corn will show you a structure rather similar to the other grains. You will find a well-developed pericarp, a crushed seed coat, a unicellular aleurone layer, and finally the starch-bearing endosperm (nutritive tissue) (Fig. 16).

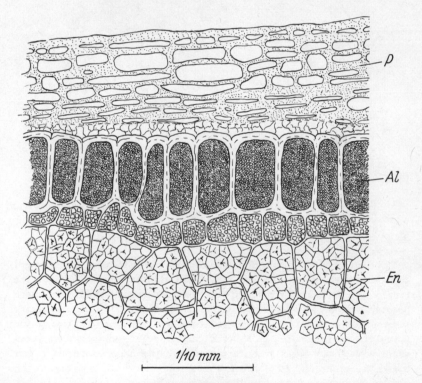

1/10 mm

Fig. 16. Corn (maize). Cross-section of the edge of a kernel. P=pericarp; Al=aleuron layer; En= starch-containing endosperm.

You will also need surface sections to be able to study the structure of the pericarp thoroughly. They will show that the outermost layers of cells consist of longitudinal cells, the next layers of cross cells, and the innermost layers of tube cells. The longitudinal cells and tube cells are important for diagnosis (Fig. 17). When you examine corn meal produced from unshelled grains of corn you will often find small pieces of the aleurone layer with the tube cells attached (Fig. 17).

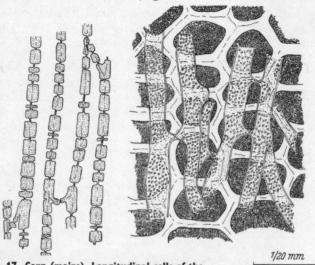

1/20 mm

Fig. 17. Corn (maize). Longitudinal cells of the pericarp in a surface view (left). Aleuron layer with the tube cells which lie on top of it in a surface view (right).

You will find two different forms of endosperm in a section through a grain of corn, even with the naked eye. Thick parts of tissue which usually appear brown are called the horny endosperm, while the more porous, white portions are called the floury endosperm. Under the microscope starch granules from the horny endosperm differ from those of the floury endosperm. Starch granules from the horny endosperm are polygonal with sharp edges and usually have a distinct star-shaped hilum (cleft) in the middle. In starch granules from the floury endosperm the corners are quite round so that the granules appear to be almost spherical. In addition, the central hilum has developed to a lesser degree or is even completely absent (Fig. 3).

When you examine corn products, the starch granules of the horny endosperm are particularly important. They can hardly be confused with starch granules of any other kind of grain.

60

FLOUR AND BAKED GOODS

Techniques of Examination

Now that you know the structure of the most important grains, you can test your knowledge in practical investigations. The examination of flour —its composition, additives and adulterants—is one of the most frequently encountered problems of applied microscopy.

Every examination of flour begins with the inspection of starch granules. Suspend a little flour in water on a microscope slide, cover it with a cover-glass, and then try to establish, on the basis of starch granules, from which grain the flour comes. You will be able to do this relatively easily with pure flours. The task gets a great deal more difficult if the flour comes from a mixture of grain, especially if one type is represented only by a small quantity. Consequently, you should also examine closely the tissue fragments which can be found—those from the pericarp and, in certain cases, also from the chaff. Sometimes—in coarsely milled flours— a sufficient number of such tissue fragments are already present in the ordinary starch preparations. However, it is usually necessary to "concentrate" the pericarp and chaff fragments.

Triturate about 5 gm. of flour with water to produce a thin paste and then add enough water so that the total volume is about 100 cc. Stir 5 cc. of concentrated hydrochloric acid into this suspension and boil the entire mixture for 10 minutes in a large container such as a heat-resistant glass beaker.

After cooling, a sediment is formed. Decant the liquid above the sediment. The sediment itself can be examined under the microscope immediately. Nevertheless, it is better in any event if you first place the sediment in a conical centrifuge tube and wait for further settling. Remove the sediment with a pipette to examine it.

In addition to this sediment test, a foam test is often recommended. Boil a small amount of flour in plenty of water. During this process a layer of foam appears on the surface; this consists primarily of the tissue constituents containing air, such as hairs, etc. Examine a sample of the foam under the microscope.

The sediment and foam tests make it possible for you to identify positively the tissue debris of grain which tends to exist here in large quantities. The structures which must be observed especially carefully have already been mentioned in the discussion of individual grains.

Microscopic examination of bread and other baked goods is more difficult than that of flour, because the starch granules are reduced to a paste during baking and lose their characteristic form in this process. Therefore, take the samples for examination chiefly from the middle of the bread, since reduction to a paste is at a minimum here. With some practice you will be able to find granules with characteristic features even in a paste.

In looking for fragments of the pericarp, which naturally play an even more important role in examining bread than in flour, carry out the sediment test again. Soften a small piece of bread in water, grind it into a paste, and boil it in dilute hydrochloric acid as described above.

Examining Spoiled Flour

Occasionally kernels germinate (sprout) while they are still on the stalk, for instance, as a consequence of damp weather. Flour manufactured from such grain is of low quality. For this reason, it is of great practical importance to establish whether a flour comes from sprouted grain. During germination, the starch is attacked (hydrolyzed) by an enzyme, amylase. Those starch granules which have been attacked by amylase are corroded to a greater or lesser degree, i.e., they look as if they had been eaten into from all sides, with canals leading from the edge to the inside of the granule. The clefts formed during corrosion can be clearly distinguished from clefts normally found in many starch granules. You can find corrosion clefts also in the outermost layers of the starch granule, since the enzyme naturally attacks from the outside. These corroded starch granules are not present in good flour.

You can perform a little model experiment to see what corroded starch granules look like. Suspend a little wheat starch in saliva. Saliva also contains an enzyme which hydrolyzes starch (i.e., splits it into sugars). If, on the next day you examine flour moistened in this way, you will find many corroded starch granules.

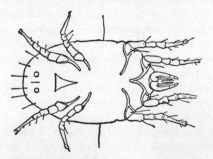

Fig. 18. Flour mite.

(Drawing adapted from Maurizio in H. Hager
and F. Tobler, *Das Mikroskop und seine
Verwendung*, Julius Springer Verlag, Berlin, 1925.)

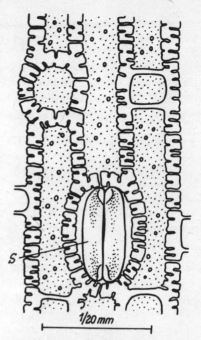

Fig. 19. A shred of the epidermis from wheat straw. S= stomate.

1/20 mm

Flour is contaminated if it is attacked by certain injurious animals or by mould. You can usually find flour mites without great difficulty. If they are present only in small numbers, shake a little flour in a test tube with water and let the suspension settle. The mites then climb to the surface and can be removed from it. If flour suspected of containing mites is allowed to stand for several weeks, the mites—if they are actually present—multiply so rapidly that it is no longer difficult to detect them (Fig. 18).

It is not always easy to detect moulds in flour. To be sure, in many cases moulds can be seen in simple water preparations (see p. 208), but occasionally it is more expedient to detect the mould by culturing it. You can find instructions for culturing moulds in Chapter 11.

POTATO PRODUCTS

Prepare a cross-section through the edge of a potato tuber between thin cork discs with a straight razor. The microscope will reveal a structure which you would probably not expect. The potato skin does not consist of typical epidermal issue, such as you know from other plant organs, but of several layers of cork cells (Fig. 20). To the inside of each cork

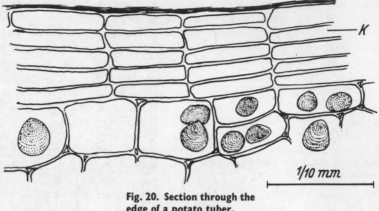

Fig. 20. Section through the
edge of a potato tuber.
K=a layer of cork tissue.

layer is attached a basic tissue of large, thin-walled cells; this is full of
characteristic starch granules of the potato: irregular granules with very
distinct rings (Fig. 21). In contrast to other starch granules with rings,
you will find that the rings here are not concentric, i.e., are not arranged

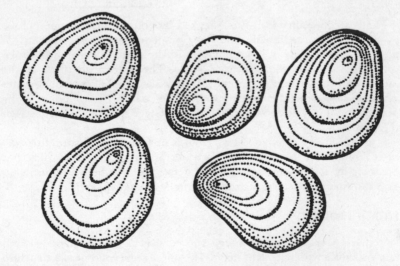

Fig. 21. Potato starch.

around a point located in the middle of the granule, but eccentric, i.e., arranged around a point located toward the edge.

It is not difficult for the relatively experienced microscopist to detect potato products—possibly in bread. To be sure, in most cases the starch granules are reduced to a paste, and the important structures can no longer be seen, but you may still find whole, undamaged cells of the basic tissue. These cells will strike you immediately by their vesicular (blister-like) shape. They are usually filled with a whitish mass which has no special structures—potato starch reduced to a paste.

You can almost always identify potato constituents with certainty on the basis of fragments from the skin, which can always be found. Naturally tiny fragments will not display the image under the microscope which you know from cross-section. In these cases you will see cork cells of the potato skin in a top view where they look the same as in a surface section. The sharp-edged cork cells appear to be contoured, because cell walls of cells situated in deeper layers shine through (Fig. 22).

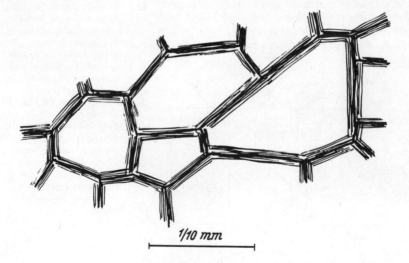

1/10 mm

Fig. 22. Top view of the peel from a potato tuber.

If a food which you want to analyze for potato shows only a small amount of potato constituents, it is advisable to use the sediment test described on p. 61. Then you will be certain to find typical fragments of the skin in the sediment.

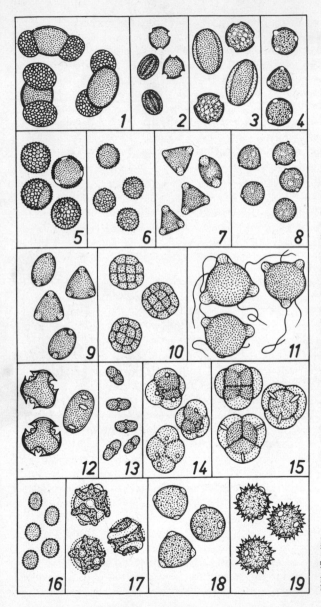

Fig. 23. Some of the pollen forms which occur especially often in honey: 1. pine, Pinus silvestris; 2. willow, Salix caprea; 3. buckwheat, Fagopyrum esculentum; 4. buttercup, Ranunculus acer; 5. lady's smock, Cardamine pratensis; 6. rape, Brassica napus; 7. apple, Pirus malus; 8. white clover, Trifolium repens; 9. robinia, Robinia pseudacacia; 10. Acacia species; 11. willow barb, Epilobium angustifolium; 12. linden, Tilia platyphyllos; 13. chervil, Anthriscus silvestris; 14. ling, Calluna vulgaris; 15. Rhododendron species; 16. Phacelia tanacetifolia; 17. dandelion, Taraxacum officinalis; 18. centaury, Centaurea jacea; 19. sunflower, Helianthus annus.

(Drawn by H. Lauffler, partially in G. Gassner, *Mikroskopische Untersuchung pflanzlicher Nahrungs — und Genussmittel*, Gustav Fischer Verlag, Stuttgart, 1955; and partially from originals in the possession of the illustrator.)

HONEY

In examining honey the microscopist is often faced with the task of establishing from which part of the world the honey comes, at which season it was produced by the bees, and—more rarely—whether it is natural or artificial honey.

When you examine honey microscopically, it is best to restrict yourself primarily to the grains of pollen which are always present. Almost every plant has a characteristic pollen. Therefore it is worthwhile to look closely at pollen from the more common flowering plants. Pollen grains give important clues not only when examining honey, but other substances and foodstuffs as well.

It is advisable for every microscopist to set up as extensive a collection as possible of comparative preparations of the more common pollen grains. For this purpose embed the pollen in glycerine jelly. Since the glycerine jelly changes various delicate structures in the pollen grains a little, you must also look at fresh pollen and compare it with your preparation in glycerine jelly.

The technique of examining honey is simple. Dissolve one volume of the honey to be examined in two volumes of water. Either centrifuge or allow it to stand for 24 hours in a sedimentation jar. (Pollen grains will also settle in an ordinary conical centrifuge tube.) You should bear in mind that pollen grains contained in the air (e.g., pollen from coniferous trees) do not settle in all cases, but can also rise to the surface.

You can draw important conclusions from the type of pollen grains found and the relative proportions of each. For example, if the honey contains pollen primarily from plants which bloom in the spring, you can state with sufficient certainty that this honey was produced by bees in the spring. You may find, for example, characteristic pollen grains from *Acacia* species, and you know the honey must come from South or Central America, or perhaps the southern United States. If no pollen grains are present, or strikingly few, you are dealing with a fir honey or artificial honey. Every microscopist should know the pollen grains illustrated in Fig. 23; these are found especially often in honey. Anyone who would like to study the field in more detail must, in any case, know a great many more forms of pollen grains than this. It hardly needs to be mentioned now what great importance pollen analysis has attained, for example, in the study of swamps and in archaeological research.

3. Studying Stimulants

Substances which contain stimulating toxins, such as tea, coffee and tobacco, are classified as stimulants. It is characteristic of our times that almost everyone feels driven and rushed, so that the use of such stimulants continually increases. This is not the place to discuss the pros and cons of stimulants. The fact is that many people get fatigued at work during the day and want to do something in the evening, but cannot manage without a poison of this kind. So, the microscopist is often called upon to study these substances and their adulteration.

COFFEE

Procure an unroasted (green) coffee bean and place it in water for a few hours or days. As a result it will swell up somewhat and become soft enough so that it can be cut without difficulty. If the bean cannot be treated immediately, place it in a mixture of alcohol and glycerine and keep it as long as desired.

Upon examination with the naked eye, a cross-section of a coffee bean will show you a horny tissue. The nutrient tissue or endosperm is rolled in at the edges toward the inside and thus forms a characteristic cleft (Fig. 24). Frequently, remnants of the seed coat, the silver skin, are found in this cleft.

A thin cross-section through the endosperm of the coffee bean will show you characteristic cells under the microscope. The walls of these cells are irregularly thickened and therefore look nodulated or beaded.

 Fig. 24. Cross-section of a coffee bean.

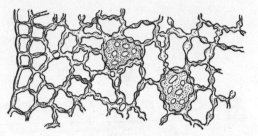

Fig. 25. Cross-section of the edge of a coffee bean.

Some of the cells in your section will be cut in such a way that their walls can be seen in a surface view. In such cells you will see large oval pits (Fig. 25).

Now pull a particle of the silver skin out of the fold in the spermoderm with a pointed pair of tweezers and examine it in glycerine. First of all, you will see a basic tissue which appears to be almost structureless, but consists of crushed, delicate cells, scarcely visible. These stone cells, stored in this basic tissue, are important, characteristic elements of the coffee bean. You not only can recognize true coffee by the stone cells, but can also differentiate between the various species of coffee. You will note that the stone cells have heavily thickened walls and a large number of pits. In *Coffea arabica*, coffee of the highest quality, you will find that the stone cells are relatively delicate, often exhibit pointed ends and have many pits on the reverse walls (i.e., walls turned toward the observer in the preparation) (Fig. 26). Stone cells of *Coffea liberica*, a commonly used species of African coffee of lower quality, are larger and coarser in structure, have blunt ends and display heavy pitting on the side walls. The stone cells of *Coffea arabica* ordinarily are located next to one another in large groups, while those in *Coffea liberica* are usually only combined in small groups.

After you have become acquainted with the most important structural elements of the coffee bean, make permanent preparations of the best sections for your comparative collection before going on to your main problem, namely, the examination of roasted coffee. It is simple and expedient to mount the sections unstained in glycerine jelly.

To examine ground, roasted coffee, crush a sample—preferably in a mortar—until it still feels slightly granular. Then place a knife tip full of the ground coffee on a microscope slide with a large drop of chloral hydrate solution (7 parts by volume of chloral hydrate[14] + 3 parts by

---

[14] If difficult to obtain, eau de Javelle may be substituted. However, be careful when using Javelle water not to get it on the microscope lens; it has a very corrosive action on glass and metal.

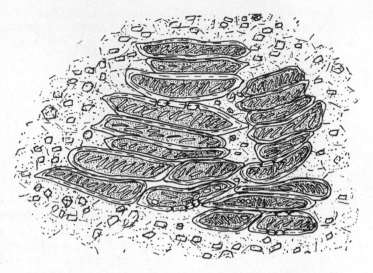

Fig. 26. A group of stone cells from the silver skin of Coffea arabica.

volume of water). Heat the slide over an open flame until the chloral hydrate solution begins to boil. Finally, replace the chloral hydrate which has evaporated and place a cover-glass on top.

The coffee granules are bleached by chloral hydrate so that the cell structures can be recognized. The bleaching proceeds from the edge to the middle of the individual fragments and reaches an optimum after about half an hour. After that the structures become blurred again, because the swelling effect of chloral hydrate takes the upper hand.

Study all of the fragments in the preparation of bleached ground coffee which still display a cell structure. You will find the beaded, thickened cells of the endosperm and the stone cells of the silver skin without difficulty. Quite rarely you will also find fragments consisting of embryonic cells which are small and uniform—remnants of the embryo found in coffee beans.

Only the constituents mentioned—endosperm cells, stone cells, and now and again cells from the embryo—indicate that you are dealing with pure coffee beans. All other tissue positively indicates the presence of adulterants.

To make permanent preparations from roasted coffee, do not bleach the ground coffee with chloral hydrate, but with Javelle water (aqueous solution of sodium hypochlorite). Suspend a sample of ground coffee in plenty of Javelle water and let it stand for one to two days in a covered container. When the powder has become light, wash it with a dilute solution of acetic acid in water, rinse with pure water, and mount in glycerine jelly.

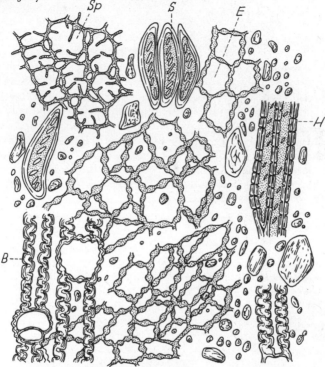

Fig. 27. Coffee adulterated with barley. E=endosperm cells of the coffee bean H=hypodermal fibres of barley chaff; B=epidermal cells from barley chaff; S=stone cells from the silver skin of the coffee bean; Sp=spongy parenchyma of barley chaff.

Coffee is occasionally found adulterated with grains. After having studied grain products thoroughly, you will be able to identify them without any difficulty. Sometimes it is wise to produce some "artificially" adulterated coffee in order to have a good comparative preparation at hand.

Besides barley, other frequently used adulterants and substitutes for coffee are various leguminous plants, figs, acorns and pears. Comparison preparations in cross-section and surface sections should be made. The pericarp and seed coat are the diagnostically important parts of these plants, and pulverizing is recommended in order to facilitate recognition when they occur pulverized in coffee.

TEA

Prepare cross-sections of freshly brewed tea leaves between small cork discs. In doing so, take care to hit the midrib too if possible.

In the cross-sections you will see, first of all, the typical structure of a leaf. The palisade parenchyma and the spongy parenchyma lie between the upper and lower epidermal layers (Fig. 28). Examine the cross-section carefully and in doing so you will discover strange cells—especially in the vicinity of the midrib—which do not correspond to the surrounding tissue, either in shape or size. These cells are called idioblasts. You cannot mistake the idioblasts of tea leaves. They are so large that frequently one idioblast passes through the entire thickness of the leaf from upper to lower epidermis. Their cell walls, usually very thick, are often sinuated and indented (Figs. 28 and 29).

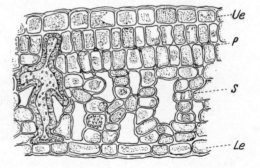

Fig. 28. Cross-section of a tea leaf with an idioblast. Ue=upper epidermis; P= palisade layers; S=spongy parenchyma; Le=lower epidermis.

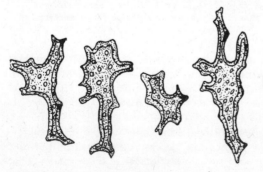

Fig. 29. Various forms of idioblasts in a tea leaf.

Inasmuch as idioblasts in this form are found almost only in the tea leaf, they are a very important characteristic of true tea.

You must still refer to the one-celled hairs located predominantly in the lower epidermis for characterization of the tea leaf. Cut up a few tea leaves which have been softened, and place them in a drop of chloral hydrate[15] solution so that the upper and lower sides face up alternately. Then cover it with a cover-glass and look for hairs under the microscope. In older leaves, the hairs can only be found with difficulty—they are present on such leaves only in isolated places. In every instance, however, the experienced microscopist will be able to find one hair or another —assuming that it is actually a real tea leaf.

You will see that in the tea hair the foot (i.e., the base) of the hair, which appears to be somewhat distended, passes into the shaft with a sharp bend. The base is pitted and the lumen of the hair (the cellular cavity) often disappears far below the point (Fig. 30).

Fig. 30. Hairs from a tea leaf.

It is not at all difficult to examine marketed tea to see whether it contains adulterants or additives. Boil plenty of the tea to be examined and, when cool, feel the individual leaves which have been softened. Real tea feels like leather. When rubbed between two fingers, all leaves which feel smooth, rough, greasy or cheesy should be suspected from the start. Select these leaves and examine them as described above, i.e., prepare cross-sections and examine entire pieces of the leaf in chloral hydrate. Then if you cannot find the characteristic idioblasts and the typical tea hairs, you have shown with a relatively great degree of certainty that there is adulteration or at least an addition of other plant leaves.

---

15 See footnote 14.

Occasionally it is of practical importance to establish whether tea comes from young or old leaves, and you can readily distinguish these under the microscope. In young leaves the idioblasts are still not completely developed, while in older leaves these cells tend to exhibit thick-walled forms (Fig. 29). On the other hand, you can find hairs more easily on young leaves (which are often almost covered with them) than on old leaves, where you must search for the hairs.

Many other plant leaves come into question as adulterants and substitutes for real tea. Rose leaves, strawberry leaves, cherry leaves, blackberry leaves and many others are often used. In this case you will also want to make comparative preparations. Cross-sections and surface sections through tea leaves and through leaves of the plants which come into question as adulterants are mounted in glycerine jelly.

TOBACCO

To become acquainted with the structure of the tobacco leaf, you will do best to use living leaves; these can be procured without difficulty in summer and early autumn. If living leaves are not at your disposal, crude tobacco boiled in water will do too.

Prepare cross-sections and, as with tea leaves, place a few small pieces

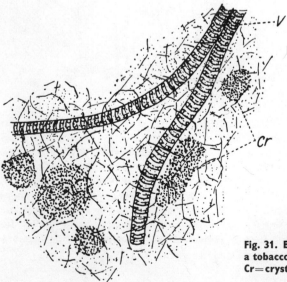

Fig. 31. Bleached pieces of a tobacco leaf. V=vessels; Cr=crystalline sand.

in a chloral hydrate[16] solution in such a way that you can examine both the upper and lower sides.

It is not always easy to distinguish between tobacco and other leaves. To obtain unequivocal results, you will have to consider the concurrence of several characteristics, each one of which can also occur by itself in plant leaves used as adulterants.

In the case of tobacco, cross-sections will again display the structure of an ordinary leaf. But you will find that many cells of the middle layer of the leaf, the spongy parenchyma, are filled with innumerable small granules. You are dealing here with fine crystals of calcium oxalate which, in its entirety, is called crystal sand. The cells in question are called crystal sand cells.

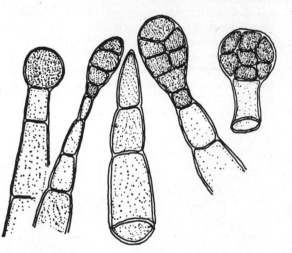

Fig. 32. Hairs from a
tobacco leaf.

Now look at the small pieces of leaf which have been bleached in chloral hydrate. With high-power magnification and intense illumination, you will find crystal sand in the form of round spots stippled with black which shine through the tissue (Fig. 31). In addition, you will notice that not only the lower surface of the tobacco leaf is provided with stomate apparata, but that a few stomata also are present in the upper epidermis. The fact that stomata occur (even just a few) on the upper side of the leaf in tobacco is an important characteristic for recognizing it when you examine commercial products.

---

[16] See footnote 14.

Hair structures on the upper epidermis are especially important in diagnosis. Look again at entire pieces of the leaf bleached in chloral hydrate solution or in glycerine. You will find many different types of hairs. First of all, you must distinguish between glandular hairs and ordinary hairs. You know that fresh tobacco leaves are sticky to the touch. The sticky juice is secreted by certain hairs recognizable by their round heads rich in cytoplasm. You will find long, unbranched glandular hairs with a multicellular shaft and a glandular head formed of several cells; small glandular hairs with only a unicellular shaft and a large, multicellular head; and, finally, long, branched glandular hairs (Fig. 32). The others are ordinary hairs which do not produce a secretion. In tobacco, they are multicellular with pointed terminal cells, branched or unbranched (Fig. 32).

Let us summarize the important characteristics in examining tobacco: crystal sand, stomata in both epidermal surfaces (in most other dicotyledenous plants only in the lower epidermis), and characteristic glandular hairs. Make permanent preparations by embedding in glycerine jelly to show clearly the structures mentioned, and use these preparations for comparison when you examine commercial products.

4. Identifying Woods

In a great many cases, wood samples can be identified only with the aid of a microscope. For example, if you want to find out what wood has been used to make a piece of furniture, the most you can unnoticeably remove is a splinter the size of a match. By using the microscope you can unequivocally establish from which species of tree the wood comes, even on the basis of a thin splinter like this.

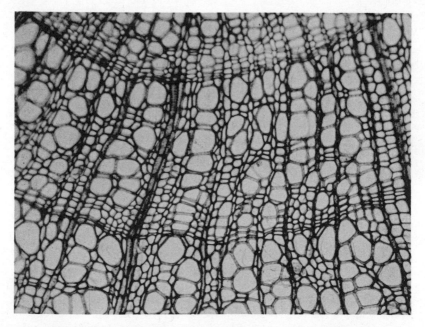

Illus. 4. Cross-section of the linden wood, general view (magnification about 50×).

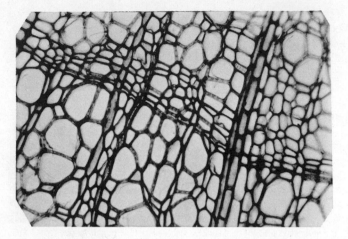

Illus. 5. Cross-section through linden wood, higher magnification (about 300×).

Before you can start identifying woods, you naturally must become thoroughly acquainted with the elements of wood.

You will have to prepare thin longitudinal and cross-sections through the various kinds of wood with a straight razor. Usually it seems almost impossible to the novice to prepare thin sections for microscopy from substances as hard as wood. In reality, wood can be cut rather easily after suitable preliminary treatment and with some experience. For example, the illustrations shown in this chapter were all drawn from preparations made with a straight razor without the aid of a microtome, let alone a special microtome for preparing wood sections.

Wood can be cut most easily when it is sap-fresh, that is, immediately after it has been collected fresh from the living tree. If this is impossible, place the wood samples in alcohol-glycerine (equal volumes of 96% alcohol and glycerine) for a few days so that they can be cut without difficulty. The samples can also be preserved in alcohol-glycerine. If it should be necessary to treat a dry wood sample immediately, boil small pieces of it in a test tube for a few minutes and then cut it.

To orient yourself at first, prepare thin cross-sections through a pine twig and through a twig of basswood (also called linden—any tree of the genus *Tilia*). Since soft woods and hard woods differ in several important points, you will need one representative of each even for the first survey.

A surface section, which is all right even if somewhat thick, should include the bark and woody tissue (xylem) as well as the pith situated in the middle. That is, it must pass through at least half of the cross-section of a twig. The remaining sections, which you will want to make as thin as possible, need be only small shreds from the different regions.

First of all, examine the sections in water. Even under low-power magnification you will see pronounced differences between tissues of the bark and those of the real woody tissue. In bark you will find cork tissue, parenchymal tissue, supporting tissue, and the sieve tubes, which serve to conduct organic substances, in an apparently irregular pattern. In woody tissue (xylem) you will see many greatly thickened cells which appear to be empty (Figs. 33, 36, 41, 43, 45, and 46). In soft woods these cells are arranged in regular, radial series (Figs. 33 and 36), while in hard woods you will not find this series-like pattern (Figs. 41, 43, 45 and 46). For the most part, these cells are nothing but cross-sectioned vessels which serve to conduct water to the living tree.

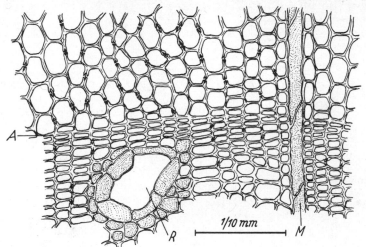

Fig. 33. Pine, cross-section.   R=resin canal; A=annual ring; M=medullary rays.

In the thinnest sections you will see a layer of small, extremely thin-walled cells at the boundary between the xylem and the bark. This layer of cells which surrounds the entire xylem like a cylinder is called the cambium. Cambium cells are embryonal, that is, cells which have retained their ability to divide. They are essentially responsible for growth of the trunk in thickness. They continually divide radially and in this way produce daughter cells on both the outside and inside. Cells which are organized laterally to the outside of the cambium differentiate into tissues which are characteristic for the (secondary) cortex. Daughter cells which

79

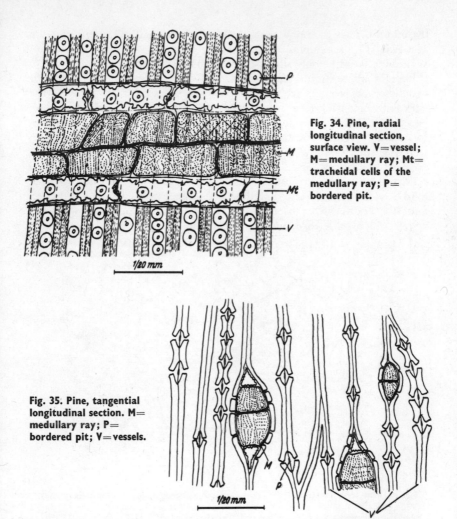

Fig. 34. Pine, radial
longitudinal section,
surface view. V=vessel;
M=medullary ray; Mt=
tracheidal cells of the
medullary ray; P=
bordered pit.

1/20 mm

Fig. 35. Pine, tangential
longitudinal section. M=
medullary ray; P=
bordered pit; V=vessels.

1/20 mm

are organized laterally inside of the cambium develop into tissues of the
xylem. It is clear that the trunk becomes continually thicker in this way
and that, during this process, the outer parts of the bark gradually crack
and split off. All of the tissue which is produced outside of the cambium,
the botanist calls phloem; all tissue produced inside is called woody tissue
or xylem. This short outline must suffice here. You will want to give
special consideration to tissue which lies within the cambium cylinder,
the xylem.

80

XYLEM

Essentially, xylem serves the living plant by conducting water and strengthening it. Accordingly, its cells are usually elongated and extremely resistant to stress and pressure. You can only make inferences about the structure of individual cells with difficulty from longitudinal and cross-

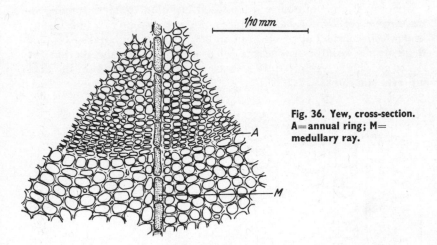

1/10 mm

Fig. 36. Yew, cross-section. A = annual ring; M = medullary ray.

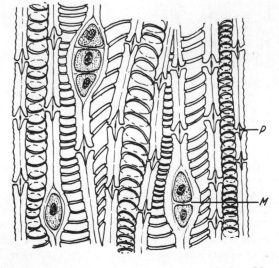

Fig. 37. Yew, tangential longitudinal section. P = longitudinal section of a bordered pit; M = medullary ray.

1/20 mm

sections. It is better to free the cells from their tissue formation and study the isolated cells.

In general, Schulz's maceration mixture, which consists of nitric acid and potassium chlorate, is used to isolate plant cells. However, it is necessary to handle potassium chlorate with some care as many mixtures with potassium chlorate are explosive. Thus, you will want to avoid using this maceration mixture whenever possible.

Split small pieces of pine and basswood into thin splinters running in the direction of the fibres and boil them for a short time in a test tube or beaker with officinal nitric acid (about 25%). In doing so, take care that there are no sensitive instruments (such as microscopes and the like) in the room where this procedure is carried out, since fumes from the acid are very injurious.

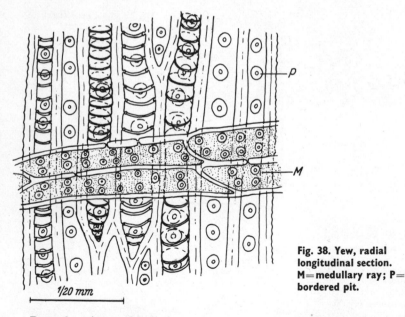

1/20 mm

Fig. 38. Yew, radial longitudinal section. M=medullary ray; P= bordered pit.

Pour the pieces of boiled wood, together with the acid, into a large container filled with tap water, swirl them around, and then fish out a splinter of wood. Wood which has received such preliminary treatment can easily be teased out on a microscope slide with two dissecting needles. (Tease in the direction of the fibres.) In some cases you can loosen the tissue formation still further before teasing it out by tapping it with a blunt object (the back of an old knife). When the material has been teased out until only a fine pulp of fibres is present, add some water if necessary, place a cover-glass on top, and examine the material. You will find all of the important structural elements of xylem among the cells which have now been isolated (Fig. 39).

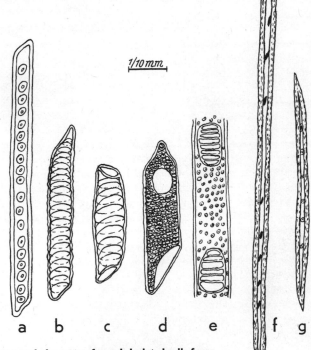

Fig. 39. Various structural elements of wood. Isolated cells from macerated preparations. a=pit tracheid (pine); b=spiral tracheids (linden); c=spiral tracheae (linden); d=pitted trachea (horse-chestnut); e=trachea with scalariform perforation of the vessels (birch); f=wood fibre (beech); g=wood fibre (cherry).

Xylem consists of vessels, wood fibres and parenchymal cells. The vessels are long tubes which run lengthwise and are made up of dead cells. The structure of such vessels will become clear to you from the history of their development. A young cell, such as a cambium cell, while it is still embryonic begins to extend in the longitudinal direction. During this process of growth its cell walls, which were originally very thin, thicken, and lignin is stored in them at the same time. However, the entire cell wall does not become thickened, as the interchange of material

83

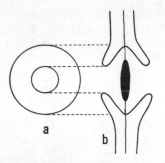

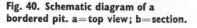

Fig. 40. Schematic diagram of a bordered pit. a=top view; b=section.

(Adapted from *Lehrbuch der Botanik für Hochschulen*.)

must still be maintained in the living cell. Isolated, tiny points in the wall remain unthickened; the cell body is separated from the adjacent cell only by the original cell membrane which remains extremely thin. These unthickened places in the cell wall are called pits; the thin membrane which separates the cells at the pits is called the pit membrane.

The vessels will serve to conduct water in the plant body and to strengthen it, and both functions require strong, greatly thickened vessel walls. Now, a great many organic substances are consumed in building the thickening layers, and the plants could very well use these at other places and for other functions as well. Consequently, many plants follow a certain course in the structure of their vessels so that a high degree of strength is obtained with the use of a small amount of material.

When the young growing cells have reached a certain thickness, only a few particular places in the cell wall are further thickened. This is done by a reinforcement of the cell wall with ridges which project into the interior of the cellular cavity. The structure of these ridges is characteristic and is often important in the identification of woods.

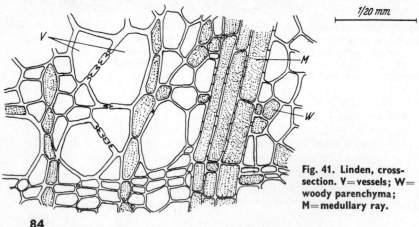

1/20 mm

Fig. 41. Linden, cross-section. V=vessels; W= woody parenchyma; M=medullary ray.

84

You have now progressively followed the development of a young cell to a vessel: extension with simultaneous thickening of the cell wall and formation of pits, accompanied in many cases by ridge-shaped reinforcement of the cell wall. Only one last step is lacking: the contents of the cell die and only the dead, lignified skeleton of the wall remains. Naturally it is tube-shaped and now it begins to conduct water. Strangely enough, in this case the cell begins to function in the plant body only after it dies.

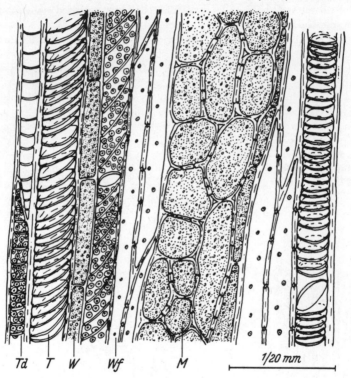

Fig. 42. Linden, tangential longitudinal section. W=woody parenchyma; Wf=wood fibre; M=medullary ray; T=trachea; Td=tracheid.

Vessels

Vessels are classified according to the type of their thickening: in the case of ring-shaped thickening ridges, they are called annual xylem elements; vessels with spiral thickening ridges are called tracheids. Quite often the thickening ridges are connected with one another in the form of a net. Such vessels are called reticulate vessels.

Not all vessels are characterized by special thickening ridges; that is, the entire cell wall is often thickened uniformly—naturally, with the exception of the pits. An especially large number of pits are present in such vessels, which is the reason they are simply called pitted vessels.

The pits of pitted vessels are usually bordered, i.e., their pit canal is approximately conical in shape. Therefore, in a top view—as can be seen from Fig. 40—such a pit appears to be surrounded by a corona. If the pits of pitted vessels extend transversely and are situated one upon the other, the top view creates the impression of a ladder. Thus, scalariform vessels is an appropriate term. However, pits of pitted vessels are usually

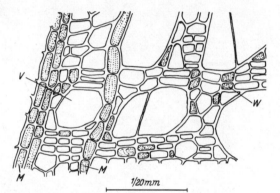

Fig. 43. Birch, cross-section. V = vessels; W = woody parenchyma; M = medullary ray.

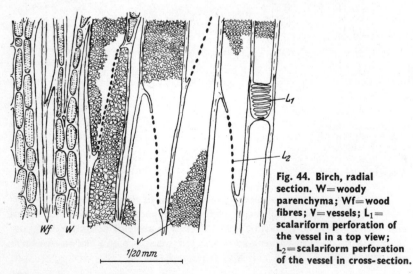

Fig. 44. Birch, radial section. W = woody parenchyma; Wf = wood fibres; V = vessels; L_1 = scalariform perforation of the vessel in a top view; L_2 = scalariform perforation of the vessel in cross-section.

86

round. You can observe bordered pits very clearly in pine which has been macerated with nitric acid.

All of these different types of vessels are either tracheids or tracheae. The difference between *tracheids* and *tracheae* can also be understood most readily from the history of their development. You have seen above how a cell is transformed into a vessel. In order to provide continuous conduction of water, continuous paths of conduction are obviously necessary.

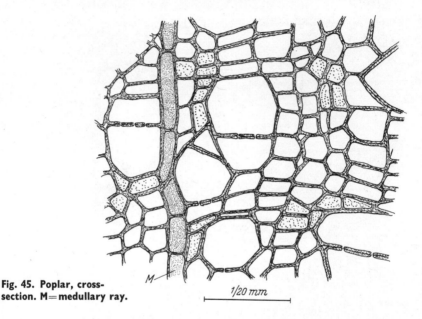

Fig. 45. Poplar, cross-section. M=medullary ray.

M

1/20 mm

Consequently, the growing cells must also become attached to corresponding cells above and below, and in their turn these must join with cells located still further above or below. You can see that in this way long tubes to conduct water are formed. In the beginning, however, these long tubes are separated by the end walls of the cells. *Tracheids* are characterized by the fact that the end walls (which usually slant) are retained. In tracheids the stream of water is conducted through a large number of pits in the end walls.

On the other hand, the end walls of *tracheae* have disintegrated and real tubes (of individual segments) are formed. The manner in which end walls of tracheae have disintegrated is an important characteristic. Usually the end walls disintegrate with the exception of a narrow border: hole-shaped or simple perforation (Fig. 39 c and d). However, once in a while the end wall does not disintegrate as a whole, but is only perforated by several transverse holes located one above the other: scalariform perforation (Fig. 39 e, and Fig. 44). You can best see whether tracheids or tracheae are present and how the end walls of tracheae have been perforated in pieces of wood which have been macerated in nitric acid and teased out. Sometimes even simple longitudinal sections show the relationships quite well.

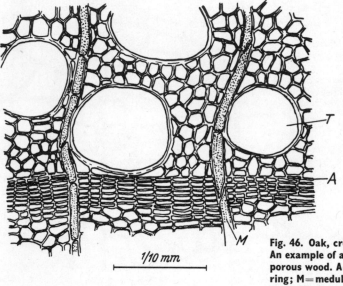

1/10 mm

Fig. 46. Oak, cross-section. An example of a ring-porous wood. A=annual ring; M=medullary ray; T=trachea.

Tissues

Wood or ligneous fibres serve exclusively for strengthening. They are long, narrow dead cells with greatly thickened walls. Wood fibres are pointed at both ends, and their pits often appear as narrow, inclined crevices (Fig. 39 f and g).

Cells of the parenchyma are easier to examine in sections than in macerated preparations. You have already prepared cross-sections of pine and basswood. In order to visualize the structure of wood correctly, you still need the corresponding longitudinal sections. The tissues of which wood is composed are often different in structure in the radial direction than in the tangential direction. In addition to the macerated preparation, you will thus need three more sections for every examination of wood:

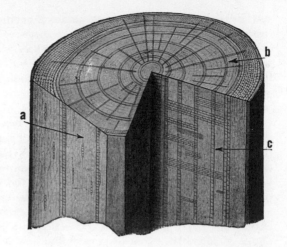

Fig. 47. The different cutting directions with cylindrical objects. a= tangential cut; b=cross-section; c=longitudinal cut through the trunk.

a cross-section, a tangential longitudinal section, and a radial longitudinal section. Fig. 47 shows the three directions in which these cuts are made.

In your cross-sections of pine you have already seen the radial series of vessels. Since you have now also examined macerated pine, you know that pine vessels are primarily pitted vessels, that is, tracheids. You could not locate tracheae and wood fibres in your macerated pine preparations; soft woods have only parenchymal cells and tracheids in their wood. You will find the other elements of wood only in hard woods, and you have already seen them, at least, in part, in macerated basswood.

Between the vessels in a cross-section of pine you will see rows of relatively thin-walled cells running radially and cutting wedge-shaped pieces out of the xylem (see Fig. 47). A cytoplasmic body can be seen clearly in the cells, and after suitable staining you will also find the cell nuclei. These rows of living cells are called wood rays or medullary rays, and the tissues that they form are called the medullary ray parenchyma (Figs. 33 and 36). In Fig. 34 you see medullary rays of pine in a radial section; in Fig. 35, in a tangential section.

In addition to the medullary rays which run radially, you will also find strands of parenchymal cells running lengthwise, the xylem parenchyma (Figs. 42 and 43). The xylem parenchyma is represented only poorly in soft woods, but it plays an important role in hard woods.

Parenchymal cells of the xylem parenchyma and medullary ray parenchyma, which are all living, serve in particular for conducting and storing organic materials. The parenchymal strands are joined to one

89

and radial longitudinal) you can obtain a good picture of the size and structure of the medullary rays.

Until now you have dealt almost exclusively with wood from the pine, an example of a soft wood. Now, in the same way, you will want to study the cross-section, radial and tangential longitudinal sections of basswood, an example of a hard wood.

The cross-section of basswood shows a quite different arrangement of the xylem elements. Narrow vessels stand next to wide ones in an apparently irregular pattern. To be sure, boundaries of the annual rings can be seen readily, but the summerwood has relatively wide vessels and they differ less sharply from the wide springwood vessels. In basswood you will look for resin canals in vain. On the other hand, the xylem parenchyma is very well developed. You will find living cells and cell groups (obliquely cut strands of the xylem parenchyma) right in the midst of the vessels and often without connection to a medullary ray. You will be able to follow their course in the longitudinal sections (Figs. 41 and 42).

Radial and tangential longitudinal sections through basswood show that, like all hard woods, it has a much greater variety of structural elements than the soft woods, which consist almost exclusively of tracheids and the parenchyma of medullary rays. Use a macerated preparation for a more detailed study of the individual elements—then the longitudinal sections will demonstrate how the cells have been linked together in tissue structures. You will find many of the types of vessels which have been mentioned above. But it is more important for you to establish that in basswood not only tracheids occur, but also large numbers of tracheae. Ligneous fibres are additional elements not encountered in pine wood. In basswood they have very small bordered pits, while in most other woods there are only simple pits.

Woods, like basswood, which display only moderately clear differences between summerwood and springwood are called diffuse-porous. A great many other hard woods belong in this classification. However, there are species among the hard woods (such as oak) which have sharp, distinct boundaries of the annual rings and correspondingly striking differences between summerwood and springwood. These are called ring-porous (Fig. 46).

Identification

You have now become acquainted with the most important structural elements of soft and hard woods. Your next task will be to identify different species of wood. It is easiest if you also make comparative preparations for this purpose. Procure samples of the most important commercial another in a network which runs through the entire xylem. Thus, you can justifiably speak of living wood, although the bulk of wood consists of dead cells—vessels and ligneous fibres.

In a cross-section of pine you will often find canals which have been cut. Their walls are formed of thin, living cells. These are the resin canals (Fig. 33).

Rings

By this time, you have made many interesting observations on your cross-section of pine. In doing so, you have certainly found that the thickness of the walls and the circumference of the vessels alternate in a certain rhythm. You will find especially sharp boundaries time and again in the cross-section between groups of narrow, thick-walled vessels and groups of broad, thin-walled vessels. These ring-shaped boundaries are nothing but annual rings which can be seen even with the naked eye.

You have seen how the cambium continually produces cells, both on its outside and inside, which are differentiated into the elements of xylem and phloem. You realize that the trunk becomes continuously thicker by this process. In winter the cambium becomes inactive; it only begins to form cells laterally again in the spring. The vessels formed in the spring serve, in particular, to conduct water; they are thin-walled and have a wide lumen (cell cavity). Vessels which are formed in autumn serve primarily to reinforce the trunk; consequently, they are thick-walled with a narrow lumen. The large, thin-walled spring vessels are joined directly to the autumn vessels, for the cambium forms no vessels in winter. Obviously, a sharply defined boundary is formed between the summer-wood (formed in autumn) and the springwood: the annual rings (Figs. 33, 36, and 46).

Soft vs. Hard Woods

Now examine the tangential and radial longitudinal sections of pine. In the radial section you will see bordered pits of the tracheids from the top, that is, each one in the form of two concentric circles. In the radial section the medullary rays are naturally encountered lengthwise (Fig. 34). In the tangential section you will find the bordered pits cut, and in order to study their structure it is necessary to have thin sections. You will only be able to study bordered pits cut lengthwise at places where the section gets extremely thin (Fig. 35). In the tangential section the medullary rays are found to be slanting. From the three sections (cross-section, tangential woods, soften them in alcohol-glycerine, and make cross-sections, tangential and radial longitudinal sections as well as macerated preparations. The sections can be embedded in glycerine jelly and be made into permanent preparations. However, you will obtain better preparations if you stain the sections and mount them in a synthetic mounting medium.

Of the innumerable staining methods which can be used, one of the most reliable is given here:

Transfer the sections from distilled water into Delafield's haematoxylin (see page 22). The time required for staining depends upon the thickness of the section and the age and dilution of the stain solution. For this reason it is impossible to state exact times. For your purposes, first try staining in haematoxylin for 5 minutes and then rinsing the sections well with tap water. Examination under the microscope will then show whether they must be stained for a longer period of time. If unlignified cell walls (e.g., medullary rays, various elements of the bark) are stained a nice blue, the length of staining was correct. If they have not been stained long enough, rinse the sections with distilled water and place them in the stain solution again. Transfer sections which have been washed well for at least 10 minutes ("blued") into 50% alcohol; let them remain for at least 5 minutes (longer does not hurt). Transfer sections from 50% alcohol into the following solution of chrysoidine Y:

Dissolve enough chrysoidine in 70% alcohol so that a sediment of undissolved stain remains even after repeated agitation. This stock solution, which can be kept well for a long time if kept closed, is diluted with 70% alcohol before use. It is largely a matter of individual taste as to how much a stain should be diluted. In general, you will obtain better results if you stain for a longer time with dilute solutions than if you use concentrated stain solutions. When this stock solution is diluted in a 1:1 ratio with 70% alcohol, several minutes are usually sufficient for staining. (However, it is advisable to first overstain sections with chrysoidine to be in a better position for the subsequent differentiation.)

The wood sections should be stained a strong yellow to yellow-brown with chrysoidine. Then place them in 96% alcohol from which the chrysoidine is quickly extracted again. Let the sections fade (differentiate) in 96% alcohol until examination under a microscope shows that the nonlignified cell walls are stained blue, while lignified cell walls are a clear yellow. After this, transfer the sections for a short time (2 minutes) into absolute isopropyl alcohol and finally into terpineol. They should be kept in terpineol for at least 5 minutes, but even considerably longer does not hurt at all. Mount them in a synthetic mounting medium directly from the terpineol or after passing them through xylene.

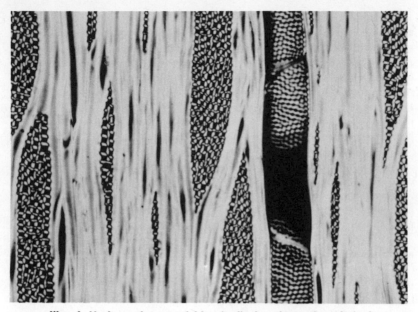

Illus. 6. Maple wood, tangential longitudinal section, under polarized light (magnification about 50×; photo by M. P. Kage).

If it should be found that the sections were differentiated too long in 96% alcohol (i.e., that too much chrysoidine was extracted), they can be transferred back from the 96% alcohol to the chrysoidine solution and stained again.

You will also want to make a permanent mount of the macerated preparation. The small pieces of wood which have been boiled in nitric acid are washed well with water, teased out on a microscope slide, and embedded in glycerine jelly. Anyone who has a centrifuge can also stain the macerated and teased-out particles of wood and mount them in a synthetic mounting medium. Washing, staining, dehydrating, and so forth are then carried out in the centrifuge. In this case, decant the liquid which has been used each time, and replace it by the next one while you stir up the material in it. In staining macerated particles of tissue, a great deal of care should be taken to wash out the last traces of nitric acid, since residues of acid will destroy the stain in a short time. It is expedient to use wash water which contains ammonia. Chrysoidine alone is usually satisfactory for staining macerated preparations; preliminary staining with haematoxylin is superfluous.

In making comparative preparations you will become well enough acquainted with the structures of various species of wood to be able to identify an unknown piece of wood without any appreciable difficulty. A tiny splinter is enough for a good microscopist to make an identification of the species. Naturally, in your examination you will remove a small splinter from a quite inconspicuous place of a manufactured article. If you want to make a reliable identification, however, you will need the cross-section, tangential section, radial section and macerated preparation in each case.

The illustrations reproduced in this chapter may perhaps be useful in your first exercises in identification. With the aid of the following chart you will be able to identify the most important commercial woods. At times, the user of the chart may come to a point where he will not be able to decide definitely which of two possible paths he should now take. In this case first try one path. If it does not lead to the goal —which you will very soon discover when identifying characteristics are no longer encountered— then go back and try the other path.

Of course, you can only use the chart if one of the woods listed is present. It stands to reason that every microscopist interested in other species of wood can enlarge the chart with his own experience in one direction or another.

CHART TO IDENTIFY THE MOST IMPORTANT COMMERCIAL WOODS

Soft Woods: Vessels arranged in radial rows in cross-section. All vessels (with very few exceptions) are tracheids; tracheae and ligneous fibres absent.

Hard Woods: Vessels not arranged in radial rows in cross-section. In addition to tracheids, tracheae and usually ligneous fibres are present.

Soft Woods

A. Without resin canals .... see I
B. With resin canals... see II
   I. —Vessels with spiral thickening ridges (spiral tracheids) .... Yew
      —No vessels with spiral thickening ridges .... Fir
   II. —Vessels with spiral thickening ridges (spiral tracheids) .... Douglas Fir
      —No vessels with spiral thickening ridges .... see 1

1. —Cells lining the resin canals thin-walled. Medullary rays surrounded above and below by cells with jaggedly thickened walls. (Latter characteristic found especially in the radial longitudinal section) .... Pine

—Cells lining the resin canals thick-walled. Medullary rays not surrounded by cells with jaggedly thickened walls .... see 2

2. Xylem parenchyma found at the annual ring boundary. In the trunk, tracheids not rare, with bordered pits not only on top of one another, but also lying next to each other... Larch

—No xylem parenchyma at the annual ring boundaries; no tracheids with bordered pits lying next to each other .... Spruce

Hard Woods

A. Cross-section shows wide springwood vessels in distinct contrast to narrow summerwood vessels; thus sharply contrasting annual rings (ring-porous woods)............ see I

B. Cross-section shows only slight differences between springwood and summerwood vessels; wide vessels also occur in summerwood so that annual rings do not appear especially prominent (diffuse-porous woods) ... see II

I. —All medullary rays single-layered (consisting of only one row of cells) .... Chestnut
(*Castania sativa*)

—Multi-layered medullary rays present............... see 1

1. —Tracheids absent, all vessels are tracheae... Ash

—Tracheids and tracheae present. Summerwood vessels arranged in undulating bands running tangentially, usually joined in groups .... Elm

—Tracheids and tracheae present. Summerwood vessels in tortuous, radial rows......... Oak

II. —Tracheae with scalariform perforated end walls present; however, most have simply perforated walls .... see 1

—All tracheae show only hole-shaped (simple) perforation .... see 2

1. —In addition to tracheae with scalariform perforated end walls, tracheae with simply perforated end walls, as well as tracheids are present. There are wide medullary rays besides the single-layered medullary rays... Beech

—In addition to tracheae with simply perforated end walls, tracheae with scalariform perforated end walls are present but tracheids absent (in contrast to beech)...... Plane tree or Sycamore

—All tracheae show scalariform perforated end walls .... Birch (and Alder)

2. —Single-layered medullary rays throughout... see a

—Multi-layered medullary rays present ...... see b

(a) Spiral tracheae absent .... Poplar (and Willow)

—Spiral tracheae present .... Horse chestnut

(b) —Spiral tracheae absent .... Walnut

—Spiral tracheae present .... see *

*—Wood fibres with simple pits. (Careful study necessary to distinguish simple or bordered pits) .... Maple

*—Wood fibres with bordered pits (with others in the radial walls of the tangential sections) ...... see **

**—Medullary ray in tangential section seen clearly with the naked eye .... Cherry
(*Prunus avium*)

—Medullary rays in tangential section cannot be seen clearly with naked eye; they appear as fine lines when observed with a magnifying glass. (The medullary rays of cherry are much wider than those of linden. In case of doubt study comparative preparations.) .... Linden or Basswood

5. Examining Animal Cells and Tissues

You encounter animal cells and tissues again and again as a microscopist. Sometimes you look for them specifically, when, for instance, examining food products, urine, and stools, and sometimes they appear as incidental impurities. In any case, you must be in a position to recognize animal cells, and to identify the tissue they come from.

Tissue is an aggregate of similar cells. You have already learned to recognize tissues in plants—the epiderm, the palisade tissue and spongy parenchyma of deciduous trees, vascular tissue (e.g., conducting tissue such as phloem and xylem), and cork tissue.

The science of tissue structure is called histology. It is a widespread misconception that histological studies on animal tissues are possible only with the aid of the microtome. Certainly a precision instrument is a valuable and often indispensable device. But even in purely scientific investigations the microtome is frequently not used nowadays, because of the increasing realization that animal tissues are often easier to study in smears or teased preparations than in sections.

If you prefer to prepare sections, however, animal organs can be cut with or without a microtome. Brief instructions have been given in Chapter 1.

Living cells change extremely quickly after an animal's death. They are subject to self-digestion (autolysis), which soon alters or destroys all the fine structures. Consequently, you must use completely fresh, living tissue for this work. Kill it with suitable fixing agents in such a way that the cells will be changed as little as possible and will present a picture which closely resembles the living state.

Procure a small laboratory animal, such as a white mouse, which you can obtain inexpensively from a biological supply house. Kill the animal

Illus. 7. Villus in the oviduct of a mouse.
Example of ciliated epithelium (magnification about 500×).

painlessly by placing it in a small glass jar, put in a wad of cotton which has been soaked in chloroform, and then cover with a lid which seals it tightly.

Good instructions for dissecting small animals can be found in Stehli, *The Microscope — and How to Use It*[17]. Proceed in the same way here, but do not open up the animal under water in any circumstances, for you want to study the finer cell and tissue structures. Cut the peritoneum along the median line with a sharp pair of scissors, turn it down to the sides, and fasten it with needles to a support. Then remove the abdominal wall and expose the internal organs carefully.

One principle must be observed from the beginning: cut as little as possible. Only organs which have been completely exposed should be detached and removed. Carry out the essential part of the preparation by carefully pushing and pulling with blunt instruments, perhaps the dull edge of a scalpel or a blunt pair of tweezers.

Frogs are often recommended for this type of study. But as a friend of nature, you should not want to contribute to the depletion of native animals. Instead, use laboratory animals which can be obtained whenever needed from breeders of experimental animals.

Make smears and teased preparations for microscopic studies. Soft, spongy organs, such as the liver and testicles, are suitable for making smears, while more solid organs, such as the wall of the stomach and intestines, should be made into teased preparations.

[17] Published in the U.S. by Sterling Publishing Co., Inc., New York, and in Great Britain by Oak Tree Press, Ltd., London.

Have a few 100 cc. jars ready with a dilute solution of formalin and cover them with glass plates. Prepare the formalin solution by diluting one part of commercially available 40% formaldehyde solution with 4 parts of tap water.

Start with a smooth cutting surface when working with organs suitable for smears, touch the organ lightly to a slide which has been cleaned with alcohol, and smear the entire organ across the surface of the slide without pressing heavily. Then put the slide with the smear immediately into the diluted formol to fix the cells and cell groups which have remained clinging to the glass surface. The tissue fluid, which was pressed out of the organ during smearing, coagulates and fastens the particles of tissue securely when the slide is immersed in formalin. Further treatment only washes away crude tissue debris which would be unsuitable for microscopic study.

Suitable teased preparations are a little more difficult to make, since delicate cells can dry out all too easily during the somewhat longer process of preparation. Place small pieces of tissue on a clean microscope slide and tease them out with dissecting needles while blowing continuously. Avoid adding water or any other liquid under any circumstances. When the piece of tissue has been teased to an almost pulpy consistency, spread the material in a thin layer over a large area of the slide and immerse the slide in formalin. Leave the larger pieces which would interfere with subsequent observations on the slide for the time being. Remove them only after they have been fixed in formalin or, even better, only shortly before you mount them with a synthetic mounting medium.

Allow both smears and teased preparations to stand in formalin for at least $\frac{1}{2}$ hour (even longer will not hurt them) so that they will be fixed all the way through. Then rinse them well for at least 10 to 15 minutes in several changes of tap water, place them in distilled water for a short time, and finally, stain them by one method or another.

The simplest method, which is successful in all cases, is staining with haematoxylin-eosin. Generally Delafield's haematoxylin is used, but better results are obtained with animal tissues when Ehrlich's ácid haematoxylin stain is employed. The preparation of this stain solution is described on p. 21.

Place the slides with their adhering tissue particles into suitable jars filled with stain solution. It is difficult to say how long to stain, especially with haematoxylins—this depends not only on the thickness of the object, but on the type of fixative used, and particularly on the way the slide was prepared and on the age of the staining solution. Therefore, stain only 4 to 5 minutes at first. Place the slides in several changes of tap water until the objects which were first stained red have assumed an intense blue tint. Then check with the microscope to determine whether the staining is intense enough. If it still does not meet your requirements, then rinse with distilled water and stain again. If no distilled water is available, rinse at least 15 minutes with tap water. Ehrlich's acid haematoxylin in particular contains much acid which must be rinsed away completely if the preparations are not to fade after a short time.

Haematoxylin stains the nuclei mainly. To make the cytoplasmic structures stand out distinctly, add contrast staining with the cytoplasm stain, eosin. It is up to the individual how strong to mix the eosin solution. Strong solutions stain quickly but often result in smudging, whereas weak solutions stain slowly but neatly. A 0.1% solution is suitable. Rinse off the slides taken from the eosin solution in distilled water. They should display a definite red tint, but should not be stained an extremely bright red. Since eosin can be removed again with water and dilute alcohol, it is not necessary to be too fussy in estimating how long to stain them. If necessary, leave the preparation in distilled water or 50% alcohol until it no longer appears overstained. By the way, always avoid staining too intensely with cytoplasm stains, since under certain circumstances this can conceal important structures.

Transfer the microscope slide from distilled water to 50% alcohol for several minutes, then into 70% alcohol, and finally into 90% alcohol. From the 90% solution of alcohol, transfer it to absolute isopropyl alcohol to dehydrate the preparation completely. Therefore, keep it in isopropyl alcohol for at least 5 to 10 minutes. Finally, dry the slide well near the stained tissue particles with cotton wadding or filter paper. Drop on plenty of terpineol (not oil of turpentine!) with an absolutely dry pipette, and allow this to work for several minutes. Then blot up most of the terpineol with filter paper. Place the cover-glass on top after adding a small drop of a synthetic mounting medium.

If no terpineol is available, take the slide out of the absolute isopropyl alcohol and place it in xylene, which makes the tissue particles transparent. Then mount it in a synthetic mounting medium.

Although Domagh's method of staining with nuclear fast red – aniline blue – orange G stain (see page 26) is somewhat more complicated than staining with haematoxylin – eosin, you obtain excellent contrast with this method.

Follow the instructions on page 27 to make the nuclear fast red – aluminium sulphate solution. You will also need a 1% solution of phosphomolybdic acid in water.

Now make the aniline blue – orange G – oxalic acid solution (see page 27). After fixing and rinsing transfer the objects from distilled water to the nuclear fast red-aluminium sulphate solution in which they remain until the cell nuclei are intensely stained—which can take half an hour. Then rinse them for a short time with distilled water and stain them for 5 minutes in the 1% solution of phosphomolybdic acid. Rinse them again in distilled water and stain them a few minutes in the aniline blue – orange G – oxalic acid. In conclusion, rinse them in distilled water and immerse in 96% alcohol (for contrasting) until the nuclei stand out sharply when observed under the microscope, and the other tissue constituents appear a distinct blue (fibres of connective tissue) or orange (red blood cells). Then place the preparations in absolute isopropyl alcohol to dehydrate them. The subsequent treatment is the same as that indicated above in haematoxylin staining.

ANIMAL CELLS

From the microscopic study of plants you have become accustomed to recognizing individual cells even at a fleeting glance by the cell walls which are always clearly visible. Such cell walls, which fulfil the function of a dead skeleton in plants, are not present in animal cells. To be sure, you will find a somewhat more rigid outer zone in most animal cells; this, however, is by no means a dead supporting substance, but a thickening of living cytoplasm which is especially rich in lipides (see note, p. 41) or lipoids. Thus, a definition of the cell concept in animals is even more difficult than in plants. You often hear and read the explanation that "the cell is a little lump of protoplasm with a nucleus"—a very simple and easy definition to remember. However, it gives no insight into the nature of the cell and can hardly be surpassed in its superficiality. The famous histologist, Bargmann, summarized the cell concept in the following way: "The cell is the ultimate independent element of the animal body which is endowed with the attributes of life."

In the cell a distinction is made between cytoplasm, a semi-liquid substance with colloidal properties, and the nucleus, which is surrounded by a distinct membrane. The compositions of cytoplasm and the nucleus are extremely complicated. Protein substances and lipides play an important part in the structure of cytoplasm, but investigation of its fine and ultrafine structure is still in its infancy—only in recent years has the electron microscope revealed the construction of a few cell structures. However, this much can be said: there is no known phenomenon of life which cannot be traced back to processes in the individual cells. The great significance of the cell concept becomes clear from this alone. The nucleus can be distinguished from the cytoplasm purely externally by its different staining capacity and by its different chemical composition. The nucleus regulates the life processes occurring in the cytoplasm.

Animal cells are easy to study if the edge of a microscope slide is passed several times over the inside surfaces of your mouth. Cells of epithelial tissue remain hanging on the edge and can be studied directly under the microscope. If you study them in a very dilute methylene blue solution, then the staining will make even the nuclei stand out clearly (Fig. 48).

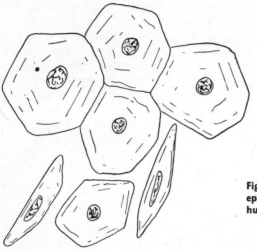

Fig. 48. Squamous epithelial cells from the human mouth.

EPITHELIAL TISSUE

Epithelial tissue is always a closed formation of cells, usually spread out over a surface. In contrast to other tissue, such as connective tissue, its cellular organization is its most important feature—intercellular substances deposited between the cells are almost nonexistent. Epithelial tissue lines all inner and outer surfaces of the body as a covering. It is found as the epidermis on external parts of the body, as the lining element of the intestinal mucosa (the mucous membrane of the intestine), as a membrane covering the bladder, and also in a modified form as the inner lining of the walls of the blood vessels to prevent transudation (the passage of serum through a membrane).

In addition, the epithelium from an internal or external surface can immerge into tissue which lies underneath, and form glands (glandular epithelium); or its cells can accept stimuli and conduct them (sensory epithelium). A popular term such as "covering tissue" does not seem very

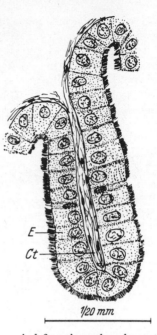

Fig. 49. Mouse: fold of the oviduct with
ciliated epithelium. E=epithelium;
Ct=connective tissue.

E—

Ct—

1/20 mm

suitable to epithelial tissues because of the varied functions they have to
fulfil. This term designates only one of its functions, that of lining surfaces.

Some forms of epithelia are:

1. Squamous epithelium
2. Cubical epthelium
3. Columnar epithelium

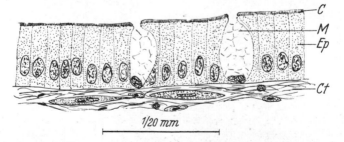

C
M
Ep

Ct

1/20 mm

Fig. 50. Columnary epithelium with cuticular edge from the small
intestine of a mouse. Ct=connective tissue with isolated
nonstriated muscle fibres; C=cuticular edge; Ep=epithelium;
M=mucilaginous cell.

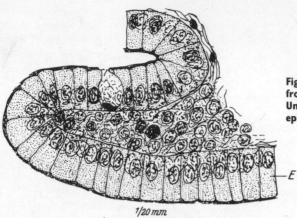

Fig. 51. Intestinal villus from the mud minnow, Umbra krameri. E= epithelium.

1/20 mm

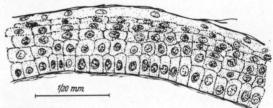

1/20 mm

Fig. 52. Layers of squamous epithelium from the surface of the tongue of the golden hamster (section 6μ thick).

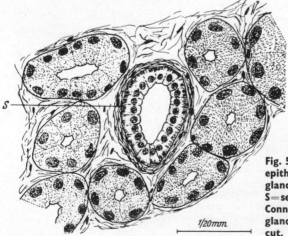

S

1/20mm

Fig. 53. Glandular epithelium. Mucous salivary gland of a golden hamster. S=secretory duct or tube. Connective tissue between glandular ducts have been cut.

All of these forms of epithelia can have one or more layers. The outer ends of the cells can have a border of cilia (small hair-like processes which are continually in motion and attached to a free cell wall—ciliated epithelium). Epithelial cells of vertebrates can become horned at the outer surfaces; they produce all of the horny structures, such as hair and nails.

You have already learned to recognize squamous epithelial cells (flat, scale-like cells) from your own mouth (Fig. 48). If you prepare mucosa from the small intestine by teasing it out, you will then find a very fine columnar epithelium. You can obtain epithelial cells with cilia from the mucous membrane of the nose. For other examples, refer to Figs. 49 through 53.

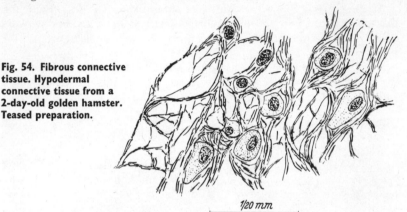

Fig. 54. Fibrous connective tissue. Hypodermal connective tissue from a 2-day-old golden hamster. Teased preparation.

1/20 mm

CONNECTIVE TISSUE

The primary function of connective tissue in the body is to link individual organs and parts of organs more or less closely with one another. Connective tissue assumes many other functions in addition to this, two of which are the storage of fat (as fatty tissue) and of water.

Here you will deal chiefly with a form of connective tissue which confronts the microscopist especially frequently: fibrous connective tissue.

The cells are not the most important feature of fibrous connective tissue, but rather the intercellular substance, the collagenous fibrils. These fibrils are very fine filaments, usually combined into wavy fibrillary bundles. Very flat cells, cells of connective tissue—fibroblasts or fibrocytes—are found in the fibrillary bundles. Collagenous means glue-producing;

105

fibres of connective tissue are called collagenous fibrillae, because they are converted into glue when they are boiled. Anyone who has seen the many, delicate fibrils of connective tissue will understand immediately that this tissue fulfils its function as a binding substance very well.

If you pull an animal's skin from the covering of muscles lying beneath, you will find a delicate white membrane between the skin and the layer of muscles. Place a small piece of this membrane on a microscope slide; spread it out as smoothly and as far as possible with dissecting needles, blowing on it continuously. Then fix it with formalin and stain it, if possible, with nuclear fast red – aniline blue – orange G – oxalic acid (see page 27). All of the elements of fibrous connective tissue can be seen when you look at them with a microscope (Fig. 54).

Another class of connective tissue is reticular tissue. The cells of reticular tissue branch out into star-shaped formations and are joined in a network with very large meshes. Many elastic fibres are accumulated around the cells.

Reticular tissue is hardly ever found alone. It forms the foundation of the lymphatic organs (for example, the spleen, lymph nodes, tonsils, etc.), which consist largely of reticular tissue. The number of white blood cells

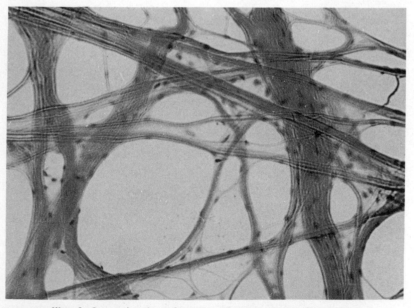

Illus. 8. Connective tissue from the greater or gastrocolic omentum (magnification about 120×; photo by F. Bode).

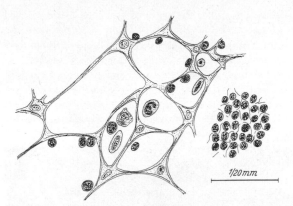

1/20mm

Fig. 55. Reticular connective tissue from the head kidney (pronephros) of the mud minnow, Umbra krameri. Crushed preparation. Individual particles were rinsed well with physiological saline solution. In this way, white blood cells (especially lymphocytes) were largely washed out from the meshes of the reticulum. At the right is a piece of the pronephros without removal of the lymphocytes. The reticulum is completely covered by the mass of white blood cells.

1/20mm

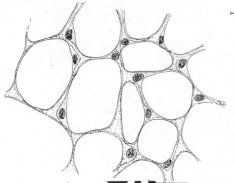

Fig. 56. Section of the fatty tissue from one of the lobes of fat which surround the ovary of a mouse. The globules of fat have been dissolved from the cells.

(lymphocytes) in these organs is so large that reticular tissue is completely concealed and you cannot even see it at all without preliminary treatment.

With a little bit of luck, the reticular tissue can be made visible. Tease out a small piece of tissue from a lymph organ, such as the spleen. Then shake the small particles of tissue well in a small test tube with physiological saline solution (0.75–0.9%). Doing this partially rinses the white blood cells out of the meshes of reticular tissue (Fig. 55).

Fatty tissue consists of large, blister-like cells (vesicular) inside which a large drop of fat is enclosed. This drop of fat is often so large that the cytoplasm surrounds it as a narrow border (Fig. 56).

107

CARTILAGENOUS TISSUE (Cartilage)

Cartilage belongs to the group of supporting tissues, along with connective tissue. We find that intercellular substance also predominates in cartilage, in comparison with which the cells are unimportant. Cartilage can be cut adequately with a razor-blade, so you can even prepare sections of this tissue without great difficulty. Cross-sections through costal (rib) cartilage, for example, can give very impressive images under the microscope.

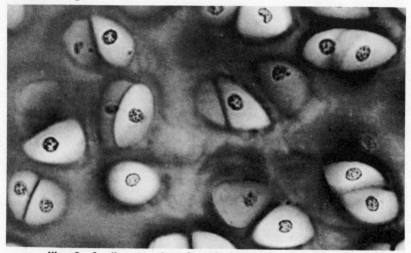

Illus. 9. Cartilagenous tissue from the larynx of a fire-bellied toad (magnification about 500×; photo by M. P. Kage).

You will find that cartilagenous cells (chondrocytes) are embedded in a structureless matrix (interstitial substance). The cytoplasm in cartilagenous cells tends to contract irregularly during fixing, which causes the cavity in the matrix in which the cells are embedded to become visible. These are actually called cartilagenous cavities. Each cartilagenous cavity is surrounded by a cartilage capsule, a zone of the matrix which can be stained intensely with haematoxylins.

Cartilage is much more widely distributed in embryos and very young animals than in adults. Large portions of the bones are composed of cartilage at first, this tissue serving only as a "space holder" for the bony tissue which develops later.

Fig. 57, a line drawing, can give only a rough impression of cartilage. In any case, the preparation itself will show the microscopist more than a good illustration.

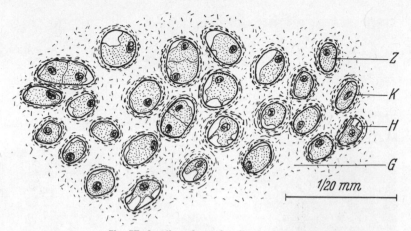

Fig. 57. Cartilage from the rib of a 2-day-old golden hamster. Section 6μ thick. G=interstitial substance; H=cartilage cavity; K=cartilage capsule; Z=cartilagenous cell.

MUSCULAR TISSUE

Muscular tissue, because its elements have the characteristic of being able to contract, gives the body its ability to move. It is a fibrous tissue, but its fibres are quite different in nature from fibres of connective tissue: Muscle fibres are constructed of cells and therefore are not intercellular substances.

Very fine fibrillae (myofibrillae) are embedded in the cytoplasm of muscle fibres, and are the actual contractile elements. A distinction is made between striated and nonstriated muscles. Striated muscles can be moved voluntarily; they are also called skeletal muscles because of their points of attachment. Nonstriated or smooth muscles, constituting a large part of the walls of the intestines, stomach and bladder, are not subject to a person's will.

Many cell nuclei, situated one behind the other, are found at the edge of a striated muscle fibre (Fig. 58). This indicates that this fibre does not consist of a single cell, but of many, the boundaries of which cannot be recognized. Muscle fibre is surrounded by a delicate membrane, the sarcolemma.

You will see a slight longitudinal striation with strong magnification; the transverse striation can be observed even under low-power magnification. What causes this striking transverse striation? You have seen that delicate myofibrillae are scattered in the cytoplasm of muscle fibres. These myofibrillae are arranged parallel to one another and pass length-

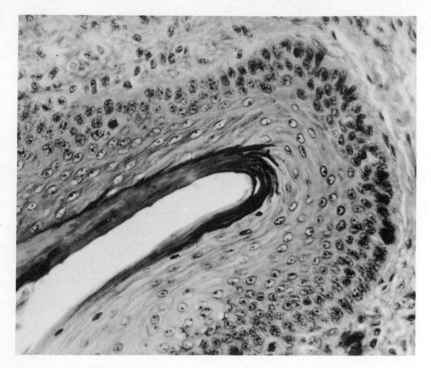

Illus. 10. Section of the human femur. Bone cells with processes (magnification about 500×).

wise through the muscle fibre. The longitudinal (lengthwise) striations can be traced back to this. Myofibrillae of transversely striated fibres are built up of very thin layers (lamellae) which are alternately simply refracting and doubly refracting (birefringent). In all myofibrillae of muscle fibres all of the simply refracting lamellae and all of the birefringent ones are located approximately in a single plane. You therefore will readily understand that the entire fibre must appear transversely striated because of this.

Individual muscle fibres are embedded in a delicate connective tissue, the endomysium. In each case, several fibres are combined into a bundle by a somewhat stronger connective tissue, the perimysium (Figs. 58 and 59).

Nonstriated muscles are much simpler in structure than striated ones, the individual muscle fibres being spindle-shaped individual cells with

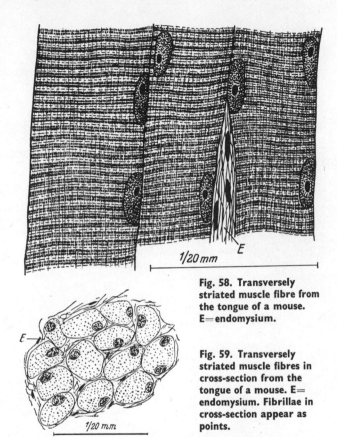

Fig. 58. Transversely striated muscle fibre from the tongue of a mouse. E=endomysium.

Fig. 59. Transversely striated muscle fibres in cross-section from the tongue of a mouse. E= endomysium. Fibrillae in cross-section appear as points.

only a single slender, oblong nucleus located in the middle (Fig. 60). They also contain myofibrillae, but these are not made of alternating simply and doubly refracting layers. Myofibrillae of nonstriated muscles are difficult to recognize. When you have a good view of them, you will find them in the form of a slight longitudinal striation of the fibre.

Cut a piece from a leg muscle, tease it out in the direction of the fibre, and then study it in water without stain. You can treat more material as described above without the addition of water. Transverse striation in stained preparations appears most clearly if it is stained for several hours with Delafield's haematoxylin diluted with distilled water. You will not need to use contrast stain in this instance.

It should be mentioned here that the transverse striation of muscle fibres can be seen particularly well in insect muscles. The leg muscles

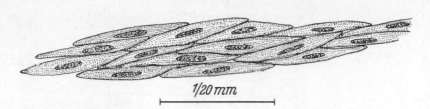

1/20 mm

Fig. 60. Muscular membrane formed from nonstriated muscle cells from the air bladder of the mud minnow, Umbria krameri. Teased preparation.

of beetles are excellently suited for microscopic observation. Of course, their fibres are constructed somewhat differently from the muscle fibres of vertebrates.

To obtain nonstriated muscle cells, tease out the wall of the intestine, stomach, or bladder. You will find isolated nonstriated muscle fibres in the preparation along with epithelial cells and connective tissue.

Illus. 11. Squamous epithelium from the tongue of a cat (magnification about 300×). See epithelial tissue (page 102).

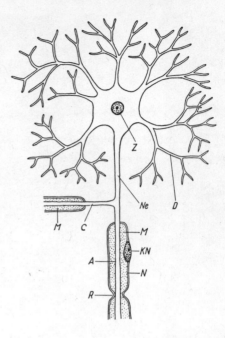

Fig. 61. Schematic diagram of a neuron. A=axis-cylinder; D=dendrites; C=collateral; KN=nucleus of the neurilemma; M=medullary sheath; N=neurilemma; Ne=axon; R=Ranvier's node; Z=cell body of the nerve cell.

(Drawing adapted from S. von Schumacher, *Grundriss der Histologie des Menschen*, Springer-Verlag, Vienna, 1943.)

NERVE TISSUE

Nerve tissue consists of elements which conduct stimuli (the nerve cells with their nerve fibres), and of a cellular supporting tissue and parenchyma (the neuroglia).

Each nerve cell sends out processes, one of which, the axon, is the essential element of the nerve fibre. Besides the axons, many nerve cells have still other branching processes, the dendrites, which are connected with analogous processes from other nerve cells. A nerve cell with all of its processes is called a neuron (Fig. 61).

Nerve fibres are not independent structures, but parts of nerve cells. A nerve fibre may be surrounded by a delicate homogeneous sheath (neurilemma, or sheath of Schwann) provided at intervals with flattened nuclei. In the higher animals many nerve fibres (distinguished as white or medullated) have, immediately surrounding the axis-cylinder, a sheath of white fatty substance (myelin) making up the medullary sheath, which is interrupted at intervals by constrictions (nodes of Ranvier). Fibres lacking the medullary sheath are said to be nonmedullated or grey.

Illus. 12. Transversely striated muscles from a frog (magnification about 450×; photo by M. P. Kage). See muscles (page 109).

Accordingly, we can distinguish between the following forms of nerve fibres:

1. Medullated (myelin-containing) nerve fibres with a neurilemma.
2. Medullated nerve fibres without a neurilemma.
3. Nonmedullated nerve fibres without a neurilemma.
4. Nonmedullated nerve fibres with a neurilemma.

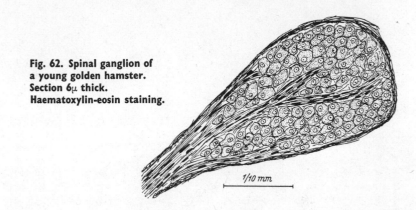

Fig. 62. Spinal ganglion of a young golden hamster. Section 6μ thick. Haematoxylin-eosin staining.

1/10 mm

Nerve fibres are embedded in connective tissue, the endoneurium. Several nerve fibres are united into bundles by a firmer layer of connective tissue, the perineurium. Finally, several bundles of fibres are surrounded by a connective tissue called the epineurium, which unites them into nerves.

To study nerve cells, place a piece of spinal cord in a very dilute solution of chromic acid for about a week. Romeis recommends 5 cc. of a 0.05% chromic acid solution in 45 cc. distilled water; the solution should not cover the pieces of tissue entirely. After this you can easily isolate and examine the nerve cells by tapping the tissue and teasing it out with dissecting needles. Unfortunately, this method cannot be recommended for making permanent preparations. The usual staining methods fail on nerve tissue, and for this reason very complicated methods are needed to make permanent preparations. Occasionally you can obtain under the microscope impressive images of nerve cells with sections through nerve nodes (ganglia) with ordinary haematoxyline-eosin stain, but even here the processes of individual cells can never be seen with sufficient contrast (Fig. 62).

To study nerve fibres prepare a free nerve, fasten a piece of it on a splinter of wood, and place it in 0.5% osmic acid for about 24 hours. Then wash it for ½ hour in distilled water and transfer it to a mixture of glycerine and water for 2 hours. Finally, place the nerve in pure glycerine and after 2 hours reduce it to fibres on a microscope slide. In successful preparations the myelin sheath appears black and the axis-cylinder bright yellow.

115

6. Testing Blood

Blood is a special kind of tissue. Its cells are not deposited in units, but float freely in a fluid. Since blood is linked with every other tissue of the body and since there is scarcely a body function which does not show some connection with the blood, changes in its composition can be used to draw far-reaching conclusions concerning changes in the functioning of the body. It is known that in many cases of illness the physician has a blood picture made and that his treatment is largely based on the results.

If you concern yourself with examining blood microscopically, you should of course understand that it is necessary to know a great deal about body functions in order to evaluate the blood picture correctly, and that a study of the blood alone is not enough for the diagnosis of a disease. At best, you can establish that the values found are "normal" or that they deviate from the norm. Everything else must be left to the physician. You must in no case begin treatment "on your own" on the basis of a blood study you have performed.

The blood cells are suspended in a protein-rich fluid of complex composition. This fluid, the blood plasma, can be obtained by centrifuging the blood cells. It is yellow and stiffens quickly in the air into a gelatinous mass. The coagulation of plasma depends upon the fact that one of the proteins, fibrinogen, is converted into insoluble fibrin. As you know, blood which has not been centifuged and which still contains blood cells also coagulates in the same way. Coagulated blood is called a blood clot. If such a blood clot is allowed to stand for some time in a test tube, it exudes a clear, yellow liquid. This liquid, blood serum, is nothing more than blood plasma which is free of fibrin and fibrinogen.

RED BLOOD CORPUSCLES

Everyone knows that there is a difference between red and white blood corpuscles. In mammals and man, the red blood corpuscles have no nuclei. For this reason they really cannot be called cells. But, since in their precursors (preliminary stages), the erythroblasts found in the red bone marrow, they are still true, nucleated cells, and since red blood corpuscles have all of the usual properties of living cells with the exception of the nuclei, they can be spoken of as red blood cells.

The red of the blood can be traced to the red blood corpuscles. But if you study an unstained blood preparation, you will be surprised to find that the individual red blood corpuscles do not appear red at all, but yellow. Actually the pigment (haemoglobin) appears yellow in thin layers and red only in thick ones.

The function of red blood corpuscles is to transport gas in the body with the help of the pigment, haemoglobin. In the lungs they take on oxygen drawn in from the air, and pass it on to cells in the body. Conversely, they take carbon dioxide, which is formed as a toxic end-product of metabolism by the cells, and carry it to the lungs where it is finally eliminated. Incidentally, it should be noted that "internal" respiration, which is essential for the body, is the exchange of gas between the blood corpuscles and the cells, while "external" respiration, carried on by the lungs, only serves the internal respiration. Internal respiration (the assimilation and use of oxygen by the cells) is an extremely complicated chemical and physical process. A more detailed study of it gives deep insight into the laws of life. For this reason it is strongly recommended that more advanced amateur biologists study these interesting processes.

WHITE BLOOD CORPUSCLES

The white blood corpuscles are true nucleated cells. There are various types of white blood corpuscles, originating in different places, each with different functions. White blood corpuscles display amoeboid mobility. This means that they can creep like amoebae by means of pseudopodia on solid substrata through certain movements of the cytoplasm. You will understand that because of this they are capable of surrounding foreign bodies (such as bacteria) which penetrate the body, and by cytoplasmic processes, absorb them into the cell body, thus rendering them harmless.

If a suspension of India ink is injected into an animal, the white blood corpuscles will be found after a short time filled with particles of the ink. They have absorbed the particles, "eaten" them, so to speak. It can literally be called eating when white blood corpuscles absorb digestible foreign bodies. These are actually digested by enzymes contained in the cells' cytoplasm. White blood corpuscles belonging to the "myeloid series" have an especially active enzyme apparatus. The absorption of foreign bodies into the cell body is called phagocytosis.

Cells capable of phagocytosis have an important function in inflammatory processes of the body. In this process they first subject the penetrating bacteria to phagocytic action (eat them), and second they "melt" parts of the body's tissue which have been affected. They can dissolve the body's tissue by secreting enzymes, the remnants then being subjected to phagocytic action too. White blood corpuscles also remove parts of the body which have died.

BLOOD SMEARS

Now let us consider the different types of blood cells in more detail. A stained preparation is needed for this purpose.

Clean the tip of your finger with 70% alcohol and prick it with a needle which has been heated thoroughly. Wipe away the first drop of blood which appears and touch the second one to one end of a thoroughly dry microscope slide which has been cleaned with alcohol. Now touch the thin edge of a second slide to the middle of the first one in such a way that the two slides will form an acute angle to capture the drop of blood between them. Now draw the upper slide slowly back towards the drop of blood. After reaching the position of Fig. 63, and touching

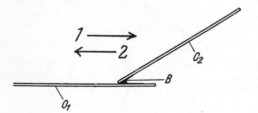

Fig. 63. Making a blood smear. B=drop of blood to be smeared; O_1 and O_2=microscope slides.

the drop of blood with the upper slide, push it slowly and smoothly in the opposite direction across the surface of the lower slide. The blood will thus be smeared in a thin, uniform layer. In this way the blood is not scraped across the microscope slide, but is drawn along behind the upper slide. The smear should be so thin that it appears faintly yellow. Smears which are red are much too thick. Under the microscope individual cells should be seen lying next to one another, never on top of one another.

A smear which has been prepared in this way should be protected from dust and left to dry in the air for at least 2 hours, but not longer than a day.

There are different methods for staining blood smears. All are the same in that an acid and a basic stain are combined. In this case the terms "acid" and "basic" have nothing to do with the pH, for example, the reaction to litmus. Acid stains preferentially stain acidophilic (acid-loving) cell structures, and basic stains the basophilic (base-loving) structures.

Two methods of staining will be discussed here. Of these, the first is recommended as a more rapid method while the second, which gives sharper images under the microscope, is recommended for studies of the fine structure.

May-Grünwald Staining

Boil about 100 cc. distilled water in a beaker, and allow it to cool again. Since the water should be completely neutral, carbon dioxide dissolved in it must be expelled by boiling. You will need the water later to dilute the stain solution.

For May-Grünwald staining it is best to buy ready-made stain since it is difficult to prepare and not worth the trouble it takes. Drop plenty of May-Grünwald solution on the air-dried blood smear and allow it to act for 4 to 5 minutes. At the same time, take care that the stain does not dry out under any circumstances. There is the danger that the solvent, chiefly methyl alcohol, will evaporate and leave only an ugly crust of stain on the smear. If this happens, additional stain solution will have to be added in the course of staining. After 5 minutes, dilute the stain solution on the slide by adding about the same amount of boiled, distilled water. It is not easy to get uniform intermixing of the stain solution with the water. Uniform dilution is hastened by gently tilting the slide back and forth. Allow the dilute stain solution to act for about 5 minutes too, then rinse if off with distilled water, and place the microscope slide vertically on one edge to dry.

The smear, when it has dried completely again, can be observed either directly with oil immersion and without a cover-glass or, preferably, mounted in a synthetic mounting medium and covered with a cover-glass. Canada balsam is not suitable for mounting blood smears as it causes fading when it becomes acid.

Pappenheim's Staining Procedure

Prepare this solution in advance: Dissolve 10 drops of Giemsa solution (which may be obtained ready for use) in 10 cc. of boiled, distilled water.

Pass the air-dried blood smear two or three times high over a small flame with the smear turned upwards. The underside of the slide should become only warm enough so that it does not feel uncomfortable when touched to the back of your hand. Then cover the smear with undiluted May-Grünwald solution and allow it to act for only 3 minutes. Finally, dilute the May-Grünwald solution by adding 3 to 4 times its volume of boiled, distilled water. Allow the dilute solution to act for 1 minute. Then pour it off and rinse the slide with the Giemsa solution you prepared in advance.

After rinsing the smear with 2 or 3 cc. of the Giemsa solution, drop the same solution on the smear again and allow it to act for 20 minutes this time. You must again be careful here to prevent the stain from precipitating by evaporation of the solvent. If necessary, add more dilute Giemsa solution in time to prevent this.

After 20 minutes rinse the stain solution off with distilled water and set the slide up to dry. Mount in a synthetic mounting medium.

Hints About Staining

Here are a few more remarks on the two procedures for staining blood:

It is important that the distilled water be free of acid and base. Water always contains carbon dioxide, which can be expelled by boiling, but water which is contaminated by other substances cannot be used at all. If you want to test water for its pH, then use this very simple method, which is more sensitive than the customary litmus paper test: Add several granules of haematoxylin to 5 cc. of the water to be tested and shake it well. Acidic water will retain its original yellow shade, alkaline water becomes reddish or brownish after a short time, and neutral water, which is suitable for your purposes, becomes a light pink after 5 minutes at the most.

Both May-Grünwald solution and Giemsa solution can be preserved only in concentrated form, but not when diluted. It is therefore senseless to prepare a large supply of ready-to-use dilute Giemsa solution. It should be diluted only immediately before staining.

First look at your stained and mounted blood smear with relatively low-power magnification. You will see the many red blood corpuscles or erythrocytes which have been stained red. They appear as small discs, approximately 7.5μ in diameter, with a lighter or darker shadow in the middle. This shadow is the result of a depression on each side of the erythrocyte which, in cross-section, gives it a kind of dumb-bell shape (Fig. 64).

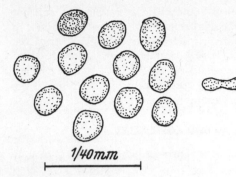

1/40mm

Fig. 64. Erythrocytes (red blood cells).

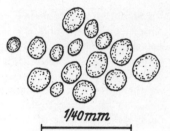

1/40mm

Fig. 65. Anisocytosis. Under pathological conditions, the red blood corpuscles can become unequal in size.

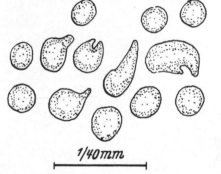

1/40mm

Fig. 66. Poikilocytosis. Under certain pathological conditions, the red blood corpuscles can assume irregular shapes.

You can see small bluish points located between the masses of red blood corpuscles under low-power and medium-power magnification. With high-power magnification these bluish points prove to be white blood corpuscles, which you will recognize immediately by their intensely blue stained cell nuclei. (As you know, there is no nucleus in red blood corpuscles.) If you examine the preparation more closely, you can make two important observations: The nucleus of white blood corpuscles often deviates from the common round or oval shape you are familiar with, and looks lobed or constricted. In addition, you will discover that all are obviously not the same type of white blood corpuscle. Let us now deal with types of white blood corpuscles in a little more detail.

The origin of the various types of white blood corpuscles has still not been completely explained by medical science at the present time. In general, a distinction is made between a "myeloid series" and a "lymphatic series" of white blood corpuscles. It is hypothesized in setting up these categories that the types in the myeloid series are formed chiefly in the red bone marrow, as are the red blood corpuscles, while the types in the lymphatic series are thought to originate in the lymph glands.

THE MYELOID SERIES OF WHITE BLOOD CORPUSCLES

Cell types of the myeloid series are called leucocytes in the narrower sense. In normal blood, the majority of white blood corpuscles consist of polynuclear neutrophilic leucocytes. You certainly found such cells the first time you examined your preparation closely. The nucleus appears to be split up into separate segments, which are often connected with one another only by fine filaments of nuclear substance. "Neutrophilic" indicates that the cytoplasm is not stained intensely with either acid or basic stains. Because of this it appears to be light blue, violet, or, only rarely, reddish (Fig. 67).

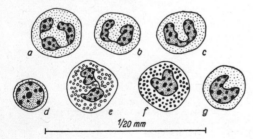

Fig. 67. Forms of white blood corpuscles. a and b=polynuclear neutrophils; c=rod neutrophil; d=lymphocyte; e=eosinophil; f=basophil; g=monocyte.

Rod neutrophils occur much less frequently than polynuclear neutrophils. Their rod-shaped nucleus is always curved and is often bent like a horseshoe, but it is never divided into segments (Fig. 67).

Eosinophils and basophils are very important in diagnosis and must be looked for carefully, since they occur only in small numbers in normal blood. However, they take on stain in such a characteristic way that once one of them is in the field of vision, you will recognize it at first glance, even with low-power magnification. Small grains or granulae embedded in their cytoplasm are stained intensely with acid stains (eosin) in eosinophilic cells, and with basic stains in basophilic cells. Consequently, the granulae of eosinophilic leucocytes appear bright red when stained, while those of basophilic leucocytes are deep blue to blue-black. The nuclei of eosinophilic blood corpuscles are generally irregular in shape and are often fragmented. Nuclei of basophilic cells are usually round and, more rarely, somewhat indented (Fig. 67).

THE LYMPHATIC SERIES OF WHITE BLOOD CORPUSCLES

Lymphocytes are a common type of white blood cell. They are one of the most important constituents of lympho-reticular and lympho-epithelial tissue, of which the lymph glands are essentially composed. They are deposited there in the meshes of a network consisting of star-shaped, branched cells. (See Fig. 55.) From the lymphatic organs lympho-cytes reach the blood, where they play an important part in its cellular composition. You will recognize lymphocytes in preparations by their relatively large nucleus, which is always round. The nucleus is usually so large in comparison with the cytoplasm that the latter is seen only as a filmy border around the nucleus (Fig. 67).

Monocytes are much rarer than lymphocytes, although in their genesis they are probably closely related to them. Their nucleus is relatively large and generally quite indented or even lobed, but it is rarely a true rod-shape and is never fragmented. After staining, the nuclei of monocytes are not such an intense blue as the nuclei of other white blood corpuscles. Instead, they are apt to be a rather shiny red (Fig. 67).

DIFFERENTIATING SMEARS

A blood smear has practical importance only if the ratio of the different types of white blood corpuscles to one another can be determined. Anyone who has gone to the trouble of studying cell types closely will have no difficulty with differentiation.

First draw up a blank table like that in Fig. 68. Then study the smear under high-power magnification, preferably with oil immersion. Every cell found is shown in the table by a stroke. For example, if you find 2 lymphocytes, 1 polynuclear neutrophil, and 1 eosinophil in your field of vision, then 2 strokes are registered in the column for the 2 lymphocytes and 1 stroke each in the columns for polynuclear neutrophils and eosino-phils. When 10 strokes are totalled in the first vertical column, the cells found next are noted in the second vertical column; when this also has 10 strokes, continue to the third column, and so on to the tenth column. You will have counted a total of 100 cells when each of the 10 vertical columns contains 10 strokes. It is only necessary to add the individual strokes in each of the horizontal columns to determine what percentage of the total is made up of the different types of white blood corpuscles. Of course, when you are differentiating you must note each individual cell appearing in your field of vision and take care to avoid counting any of them twice. Therefore, begin your examination at the upper left edge of the microscope slide, proceed vertically from there to the bottom, move the slide a little to the left, and count vertically up to the top again, and so on. In this way you can be sure to avoid counting any cell twice.

Basophils					I						1
Eosinophils	I					I		I			3
Rod Neutrophils	I		I	I		I		II	I		7
Polynuclear Neutrophils	IIIIIIII	IIIII	IIIIIIII	III	IIIIII	IIIIIII	IIIIIIII	IIIII	IIII	IIIIIII	61
Lymphocytes	II	III	II	IIII	I	II	I	III	IIII	II	24
Monocytes			II	I			I				4
	10	10	10	10	10	10	10	10	10	10	100

Fig. 68. Counting chart for differentiating white blood corpuscles.

The percentages you find will permit you to draw important conclusions. The most important finding is whether the figures deviate from the norm. As has already been emphasized, diagnosis must be left to the physician.

Normal Values for White Blood Corpuscles:

Polynuclear neutrophils ...58–68%
Rod neutrophils............... 2–5%
Eosinophils 1–4%
Basophils......................... 0–1%
Lymphocytes 22–30%
Monocytes 4–8%

Small deviations from these normal values do not necessarily indicate a radical change in the body. It should also be emphasized that a beginner often falls into gross errors in method. For this reason, every microscopist must be advised to train himself thoroughly before drawing conclusions.

COUNTING BLOOD CELLS

Values which have been found for the different types of white blood corpuscles in the blood smear are naturally only relative numbers and do not permit conclusions to be drawn about the total number of blood corpuscles.

Many will be surprised to learn that, on the average, each cc. of blood contains 5 million red and 8,000 white blood corpuscles. How can such values be calculated?

A haemacytometer (which consists of a counting chamber, a cover-glass, and pipettes for red and white cells) is used to determine the total number of red and white blood corpuscles in a given volume of blood (Figs. 69 and 70). The important part of the counting chamber is the ruled counting field, which except for special work will have Improved Neubauer Ruling. Most counting chambers have two ruled fields so that red and white blood cells can be counted in the same chamber.

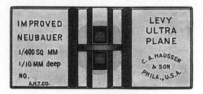

Fig. 69a. Levy counting chamber.

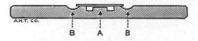

Fig. 69b. Longitudinal cross-section of Levy counting chamber with cover-glass in position.

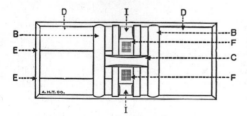

Fig. 69c. Levy counting chamber with double ruling: B=protecting trenches; C=transverse trench; D=matte pre-focusing surfaces; E=finding lines leading to ruled areas; F=rulings; I=chamber charging inclines.

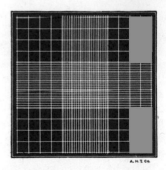

Fig. 69d. Entire area of Improved Neubauer Ruling.

(Figs. 69 and 70, and other material in this section were furnished by courtesy of the copyright owner, Arthur H. Thomas Co. of Philadelphia.)

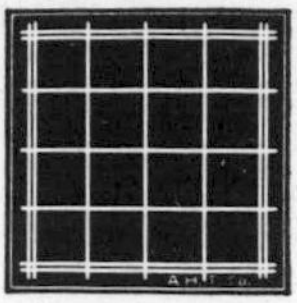

Fig. 69e. Group of 16 smallest squares of Improved Neubauer Ruling, showing transparent boundary enclosed between two engraved furrows.

Fig. 69h. Cross-section of bulb of Thoma diluting pipette.

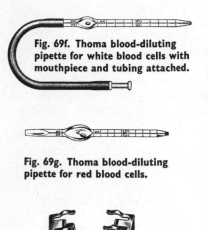

Fig. 69f. Thoma blood-diluting pipette for white blood cells with mouthpiece and tubing attached.

Fig. 69g. Thoma blood-diluting pipette for red blood cells.

Fig. 69k. Cover-glass clips.

Fig. 69j. Trenner blood-diluting pipettes and cross-section of bulb. The Trenner pipette is made by fusing to a separately made bulb a piece of straight capillary tubing whose upper end terminates abruptly in a square cut, ground, and polished surface as shown. The volume of this piece of tubing is adjusted to be exactly 1/20, 1/200, or 1/10 of the total volume of the bulb of the pipette. No mark is necessary on the capillary tube since it is filled completely. The customary dilution mark is provided on the upper stem.

The entire area of the ruling is 9 sq. mm. (Fig. 69d), and the space between the counting field and the cover-glass is exactly 0.1 mm. As you can see in Fig. 69d, the middle square of the nine has been further sub-divided into 400 small squares, each with an area of 1/400 sq. mm. For the purpose of orientation, the 25 groups of 25 small squares in the middle and the four corner groups of 16 small squares (see Fig. 69e) have a translucent boundary formed by the correct juxtaposition of the engraved lines. The groups of small squares in the middle square millimetre are used in counting erythrocytes; the corner square millimetres, in counting leucocytes.

Since the surface areas as well as the height of the liquid between the area and the cover-glass are known, it is a simple matter to calculate the exact volume. Thus, the microscopically small bodies contained in the liquid can be counted with the microscope and the values for a single cc. easily determined.

If you were simply to place a drop of blood on the counting chamber, you would never be able to see individual blood corpuscles on account of the many cells. For this reason you must mix the blood with suitable diluents. Special mixing pipettes are used for this purpose so that the amount of blood and the extent of dilution are known (Figs. 69 f–j).

General Procedure

Naturally, the ruled area, the surface of the glass slide, and the cover-glass must be carefully cleaned and absolutely free from dust or lint before use. The counting chamber should be thoroughly cleaned immediately after use by washing in filtered or distilled water and rinsed with a few drops of alcohol and finally dried with ether. If this is not done, the engraved lines will be partly obliterated by the accumulated debris from disintegrated cells. If diluted blood has been allowed to remain on the slide, it may be necessary, before washing, to immerse the slide in a cleaning fluid such as potassium bichromate and sulphuric acid. Such a strong cleaning agent may not be necessary. You can also clean the chambers by passing them through a sequence of water, alcohol, and ether (or water and acetone), which is the same procedure used with pipettes. Dry with warm dry air (your breath contains too much moisture to be satisfactory for this purpose).

The cover-glass must be placed in position over the ruled area of the slide before any solution is introduced, using gentle pressure with the fingertips, or preferably with a soft rubber stopper or velvet-faced cork, directly above the supporting surfaces to ensure the coincidence of the under-surface of the cover with the supporting surface of the slide. Or use a pair of accurately gauged cover-glass clips (Fig. 69k), which effectively prevent any disturbance of the distribution of the cells during manipulation. While continuing the pressure, slide the centrally placed clips into position simultaneously.

Remove a drop of blood from the tip of the finger in the same way as in preparing a smear, wipe the first drop off, suck the second drop up into a pipette. (See the special instructions below for the different procedures with red and white blood cells.) Use your breath—not the tip of your tongue—to control the levels of the fluids in the pipette. Wipe off the outside of the pipette and draw the appropriate diluting solution promptly to the mark engraved above the bulb, while subjecting the pipette to semi-rotations between thumb and forefinger. Close the tip with your finger. Then sharply kink the rubber tubing over the end of the pipette and place your thumb over the kinked tubing. Shake the pipette for 3 minutes. It should not be revolved continuously in one direction, shaken

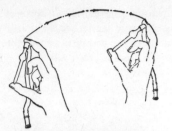

Fig. 70a. Method of shaking a pipette.

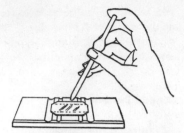

Fig. 70b. Method of charging a counting chamber.

A

A ——————— B

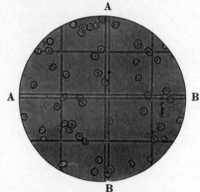

B

Fig. 70c. Correct focusing for erythrocyte count.

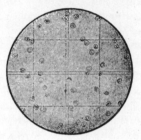

Fig. 70d. Incorrect focusing for erythrocyte count.

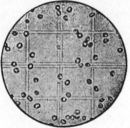

Fig. 70e. Correct focusing for leucocyte count.

in the direction of the longitudinal axis, or held in a vertical position. Consecutive counts from the same pipette dilution will differ unless the pipette is again thoroughly shaken before the count is repeated (Fig. 70a).

Remove the rubber tubing and discard two or three drops from the pipette, i.e., the diluting-fluid content of the capillary and, *without loss of time*, using the forefinger as a controlling valve, allow to form at the tip a drop of the suspension, sufficiently large to cover the ruled area without overflow into the moat. Do not use too small a dilution. The usual ratios are 1 : 20 for white blood corpuscles, 1 : 200 for red. If, for instance, the number of white blood corpuscles were greatly increased (leucocytosis), the counting chamber would be "flooded" with white cells if the dilution were only 1 : 10.

The end of the polished surface bearing the ruling is quickly touched with the tip of the pipette, allowing the drop of suspension to flow under the cover-glass. The suspension should not overflow into the moats on either side, nor should any bubbles form under the cover-glass (Fig. 70b). Allow 3 minutes for setting.

With the counting chamber in horizontal position on the microscope stage, direct the light, lower the condenser and reduce the light to a narrow pencil by means of the iris diaphragm or, in the absence of a condenser, control it by concave mirror and diaphragm alone. To direct the illumination rapidly: first, remove the ocular and, as you look at the source of illumination down the draw-tube through the objective which has been approximately focused, incline the plane mirror and manipulate the condenser and iris. This method always assures a sharply defined picture of the ruling, well illuminated to the edge of the field, without loss of time. Because of uniformity and ease of regulation, illumination from an artificial source is recommended. The light must be correctly directed and its volume reduced before finding and focusing the ruling.

Now use the finding line to locate the ruled area after having pre-focused the microscope (low-power objective) on the matte focusing surface of the chamber. Without disturbing the focus, locate and follow the finding line until the outlines of the ruling and the blood cells come into view. Focus upwards (not downwards) to sharpen the image of the cells and the ruling simultaneously. If the objectives are pre-focalized on the revolving nosepiece, the higher power objective can now be brought into accurate focus. After some experience, focusing on the matte surface and observation of the ruling and cells can be accomplished with either objective without changing (see Figs. 70 c–e).

In making counts, include all corpuscles touching the lines on the *top* and *one* adjacent side of each square and *not* those touching the bottom and the other side. Corpuscles can be counted more quickly and conveniently in groups of two. In the same manner, when using the transparent boundary around the groups of squares as a guide, the count should be made from one transparent boundary to the next, including the cells touching—but not beyond—these boundary lines.

The distribution of cells is unusually uniform, as there is no disturbance of the cells by pressure on the cover-glass after filling. (This procedure was usually followed in order to produce Newton's interference rainbow rings in the original Thoma and original Neubauer chambers with polished cover-glass supporting surfaces.) Accuracy of count, averaged from the number of cells in a minimum of squares, is thereby assured. If the count from smallest square to smallest square varies by more than 10 in the case of white blood cells, or 20 in the case of red blood cells, the chambers should be recharged and the count started again.

The older method of filling, in which the cover-glass is positioned after placing the drop, is not recommended. That method gives too high a count because many cells fall to the ruled surface before the cover-glass, which limits the depth of the cells, can be placed.

Counting of Red Cells

In counting red cells, a pipette dilution of 1 : 200 is usually used and 80 of the smallest squares counted, i.e., 5 groups of 16. To the number of red cells counted, 4 ciphers are added, the result being the number of red cells per cc. of undiluted blood. (The glass bead in the pipette is usually red.) Draw the blood up to the 0.5 mark, the diluent up to the 101 mark. By drawing the blood up to the 1 mark, the dilution would be only 1 : 100.

Example: Count of 80 smallest squares (5 groups of 16, i.e., 1/5th sq. mm.)=500 red cells.

Adding 4 ciphers=5,000,000=number of red cells per cc.

Formula: $\dfrac{\text{Corpuscles} \times \text{Dilution} \times 4,000}{\text{Number of smallest squares counted}} = \text{Corpuscles per cc.}$

Note: If metric computation is desired, count 4 groups of 25 squares each, or 5 rows of 20 squares.

Diluting Fluid for Red Cells

The most widely used diluting fluids for red cells are Toisson's and Hayem's. Toisson's is suitable for use when both red and white cells are counted, while Hayem's is intended for counting red cells only, as the white cells are not stained. Toisson's solution is not stable, as yeast spores develop rapidly—it must be made fresh or filtered each time before use. For the counting of red cells only, Hayem's is the more satisfactory as it keeps indefinitely and no organisms grow in it. Gower's solution is sometimes preferred because it prevents rouleau formation (a group of red blood corpuscles resembling a stack of coins).

TOISSON'S SOLUTION:
Distilled water ....160 cc.
Glycerine.................. 30 cc.
Sodium sulphate......... 8 gm.
Sodium chloride......... 1 gm.
Methyl violet .... 0.025 gm.

HAYEM'S SOLUTION:
Distilled water ....200 cc.
Sodium chloride......... 1 cc.
Sodium sulphate......... 5 gm.
Mercuric chloride ...... 0.5 gm.

GOWER'S SOLUTION:
Distilled water ....200 cc.
Sodium sulphate......... 25.0 gm.
Glacial acetic acid...... 66.7 gm.

A 1% salt solution may be used as a satisfactory substitute for the above, either tinged with about 1 drop of crystal violet (saturated alcoholic solution) to about 50 cc. for use when both red and white cells are to be counted, or alone when only red cells are to be counted.

Counting White Cells

The diluent for white blood cells is a 1%–3% solution of acetic acid which can be tinged with crystal violet or methyl green (Tuerk's solution). The red corpuscles dissolve in it and the white corpuscles appear clearly. Using the smaller pipette (which usually has a white glass bead), draw the blood up to the 0.5 mark and the diluent up to the 11 mark. This will give you a dilution of 1 : 20. (If a dilution of 1 : 10 is desired, draw the blood up to the 1 mark, the diluent up to the 11 mark.)

In the counting of cells, a few authorities still prefer ear punctures on the hypothesis that, due to the vascularity of the ear, a smaller incision can be made. When the finger is used, unless incision is made 3 to 4 mm. deep, allowing for the free flow of 3 or 4 drops without pressure, it may be advisable to produce hyperaemia in the hand by immersion in hot water. The hand should be maintained at the level of the laboratory table. Counts from a smaller needle puncture, necessitating squeezing of the finger, may be grossly inaccurate and worthless.

Count the cells in a total of 10 sq. mm. and multiply this count by 20, the dilution factor. The result will be number of white cells in one cc. of undiluted blood. If only 5 sq. mm. are counted, first multiply by 2 and then the dilution factor.

Some people prefer to use the following formula:

$$\frac{\text{number of cells counted}}{\text{area} \times \text{depth} \times \text{dilution}} = \text{number of blood corpuscles/cc.}$$

Here are two examples: The area of a field is 1 sq. mm., the depth of a chamber is 0.1 mm., and the dilution 1 : 10. With a 1 : 10 dilution, 82 white blood corpuscles were found in the field. Therefore, 1 cc. of the blood studied contains:

$$\frac{82}{1 \times 1/10 \times 1/10} = 8{,}200 \text{ white blood corpuscles}$$

Or at a dilution of 1 : 200, 452 red blood cells were counted in 80 of the smallest squares (=1/5 sq. mm.).

Therefore, 1 cc. of blood which was studied contains:

$$\frac{452}{1/5 \times 1/10 \times 1/200} = 4{,}520{,}000 \text{ red blood corpuscles}$$

Approximate normal values for red blood corpuscles:
In men, 5 million/cc. of blood
In women, 4.5 million/cc. of blood

Normal value of white blood corpuscles: 8,000/cc. of blood. Deviations of about 1,000/cc. from the normal value usually do not mean much with white blood corpuscles. More than 9,000 white blood corpuscles/cc. blood is spoken of as an increase, more than 10,000/cc. blood as leucocytosis, and more than 20,000 as hyperleucocytosis. In a decrease, fewer than 7,000 white blood corpuscles are present per cc. blood, and leucopenia occurs if 1 cc. contains less than 5,000 white blood corpuscles.

It should be noted that even large deviations, especially increases, need not be pathological. For example, the number of white blood corpuscles can increase considerably after eating (especially milk) and after hard work. It is therefore advisable to draw the patient's blood in the morning before he has had breakfast.

Nonpathological deviations from normal values occur more frequently with red blood corpuscles than with white ones. For example, it is well known that the red blood count increases considerably in people living at high altitudes. If you should find values in your own blood which deviate slightly from the norms given above, you need not worry if you feel well otherwise. During the period when you are inexperienced, you should always consider the possibility of error in method as well.

CALCULATION OF ABSOLUTE VALUES FOR WHITE BLOOD CORPUSCLES

On the basis of a stained smear, you have determined the ratio in which the different types of white blood corpuscles are related to one another. With the aid of a counting chamber you have also found the total number of cells per cc. It is now very easy to determine the total number of a given type of blood corpuscle. For example: In one cc. of blood, 8,000 white blood corpuscles were found. In a smear preparation, 60% of these were polynuclear neutrophils. Therefore, 1 cc. blood contains:

$$\frac{8,000 \times 60}{100} = 4,800 \text{ polynuclear neutrophils}$$

Every microscopist can prepare and study a blood smear inexpensively. Of course, a counting chamber is an indispensable necessity in counting blood cells. Unfortunately, counting chambers are not exactly low-priced. However, it is highly recommended that you obtain one, since counting chambers can also provide valuable service in other investigations. You can use counting chambers to count bacteria and other unicellular organisms, in many quantitative studies of plankton, and in every case where microscopically small bodies suspended in a liquid must be counted. (Of course, there are also special counting chambers with other rulings for these specialized purposes.) The counting chamber may even be used as an object micrometer, since a side of one of the smallest squares is exactly 0.05 mm. long.

Anyone who does not have a counting chamber available need not be prevented from carrying out blood studies for this reason. The study of a smear alone also gives interesting results.

7. Analyzing Urine

Microscopic study of the urine is easy to carry out, but it requires painstakingly neat work, especially if the urine is from patients with urinary diseases. Ordinarily, particles floating in the urine are concentrated for an investigation by centrifuging. An ordinary hand centrifuge, such as is used for plankton studies, is completely satisfactory. Anyone without a centrifuge can also concentrate the constituents of urine by allowing the urine sample to stand for several hours in a conical test tube and then studying the sediment with a microscope. Of course, the latter method is not as good as centrifuging.

You can find cells and shreds of tissue from the entire urinary tract (kidneys, ureter, bladder, and urethra) in normal urine or in that obtained under pathological conditions. In addition, noncellular elements, such as casts and various crystals, are also of great importance in diagnosis.

Just as with a blood study, a urine study alone is not enough to diagnose a disease. The final opinion in cases which seem pathological must always be left to a physician.

At least two chemical tests that everyone can perform without trouble are necessary for every urine study, even microscopic ones: the reaction for sugar and the reaction for albumin.

DETERMINATION OF SUGAR

You probably know that the dreaded disease, diabetes, is caused by insufficiency of a group of hormonal glands in the pancreas called the islands of Langerhans. If the islands of Langerhans fail to produce the hormone, insulin, or if it is present only in insufficient amounts, the body can no longer convert sugar to an insoluble form and store it. The sugar content of the blood then increases and sugar is excreted by the kidneys. If sugar is found in the urine, this can be a serious symptom, but it is still not proof that diabetes is actually present. There are, to be sure, several other reasons for finding sugar in the urine. This can happen if a certain threshold value in the blood-sugar level is exceeded by the consumption of large amounts of foods containing sugar. Above this limit, the kidneys begin to excrete sugar. In spite of the sugar in the urine, then, there is no disease at all in this case.

To test for sugar you will need Fehling's reagent which consists of two solutions kept separately:

FEHLING SOLUTION I: 34.64 gm. copper sulphate dissolved in 500 cc. distilled water.

FEHLING SOLUTION II: 173 gm. Rochelle salt (sodium potassium tartrate) and 100 cc. 15% sodium hydroxide solution mixed together and diluted to 500 cc. with distilled water.

Naturally, it is most convenient if you buy the two solutions ready-made.

Mix equal volumes of Fehling Solutions I and II in a test tube and dilute them with an equal volume of distilled water. Since the strongly alkaline Fehling's solution tends to heave (bump) and spatter when it is heated later on, measure the total amount in such a way that only the lower one-third of the test tube is filled.

Place a small sample of the urine to be studied in a second test tube. Now heat both test tubes until the liquids begin to boil. Then pour the urine and Fehling's solution together. If there is no reaction, heat the combined liquids again for a short time to the boiling point.

If the urine sample contains sugar, a precipitate intensely brick-red is formed with Fehling's solution. You can best see what this precipitate looks like by first using a solution of glucose instead of a urine sample. If you do not have a glucose solution at your disposal, the Fehling reaction can also be observed in the instructive experiment which follows: triturate (rub together) some flour, which consists largely of starch, together with plenty of saliva, to a thin paste. Let the paste stand for a while (the time required depends upon the room temperature), and then perform Fehling's test with it. Saliva contains enzymes which hydrolyze (split) the starch into sugar with many intermediate steps. Fehling's test can also be used to test juices from various fruits.

It should be mentioned that Fehling's test is nonspecific, i.e., any reducing substance in the urine will give a positive result. This is of special importance if formaldehyde has been added as a preservative.

DETERMINATION OF ALBUMIN

In almost every case, the appearance of albumin in the urine indicates that damage has occurred to the body.

Only filtered urine is used to determine albumin. Filter a large amount of urine and first test its reaction to litmus paper. If the litmus paper turns red, the urine is acid and can be used without any preliminary treatment. If the litmus paper turns blue, the urine is alkaline and must be acidified with a little acetic acid until the litmus paper just turns red. Now divide the filtered acid urine between two test tubes. The contents of one tube serves only for comparison later on; boil the urine in the second tube. During boiling, the urine may become cloudy, a condition caused by albumin or other substances. Now add 10% acetic acid drop by drop to the heated urine. If the urine to which acetic acid was added retains the cloudiness which appeared during the previous boiling, or if the cloudiness appears only after the addition of acetic acid, then albumin is present. If the cloudiness disappears when acetic acid is added, then albumin is not present but other, generally unimportant, substances are. In order to test even a slight cloudiness, hold the boiled urine which has been mixed with acetic acid next to the unboiled, filtered urine sample and compare the two liquids.

MICROSCOPIC EXAMINATION OF URINE SEDIMENT

Shake the urine sample slightly so that the particles which have settled on the bottom of the container are swirled up; then centrifuge it. To protect the centrifuge, you must be sure that the two centrifuge tubes are balanced. After centrifuging, pour off the liquid which is left standing over the centrifuged sediment, place the sediment itself on a mircoscope slide, cover it with a cover-glass, and study it first with low-power magnification, then with high-power magnification. There are urine samples in which there are practically no particles. But generally you will see different kinds of cells, small crystals, and other constituents.

Cells in Urine Sediment

You will find squamous epithelial cells in almost every urine sample. They occur either alone or in small cell formations. The occurrence of these cells in small numbers is completely normal. They are surface cells which have been sloughed off from the epithelium which lines the urinary tract. However, if the squamous epithelial cells are found in large numbers and in large cell formations, this can be traced back to an inflammation at some point in the urinary tract.

Epithelial cells from the kidney are found only rarely in the urine. They are indications of kidney disease, so you must search for them with special care. They are surprisingly small, only slightly larger than white blood corpuscles, generally round, or more rarely polygonal with rounded corners. Their nuclei are large and blisterlike. In most cases where epithelial cells from the kidneys are found in the urine the albumin reaction is also positive.

In very small numbers, white blood corpuscles are considered to be normal constituents of the urine. They appear in the sediment preparation as round, very slightly granulated particles with a nucleus which only rarely can be seen clearly. A large number of white blood corpuscles in the urine is a symptom which often indicates the presence of a suppurative process in the urinary tract (Fig. 71). If you find a large number of white

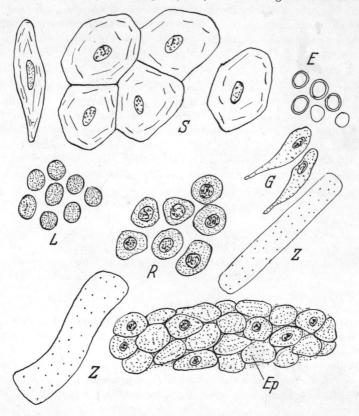

Fig. 71. The more common organized constituents from urine sediment.
E = red blood corpuscles; G = caudate epithelial cells; R = renal epithelial cells;
Ep = epithelial cylinders; L = white blood corpuscles; S = squamous epithelial
cells; Z = hyaline cast.

blood corpuscles in urine sediment, use the following pus test for confirmation: After shaking again, centrifuge the urine to be studied once more. Add a few drops of a 30% solution of sodium or potassium hydroxide to the sediment, shake it, and pour it out. If a viscous, glassy slime appears during decantation, this indicates the presence of pus.

Red blood cells should not occur in the urine of a healthy subject. Their occurrence indicates a pathological phenomenon, for some blood vessel must be damaged if red blood corpuscles reach the urinary tract. (It is well known that white blood corpuscles can penetrate through the walls of undamaged blood vessels, but never red corpuscles.) In sediment from urine, the red blood corpuscles generally look slightly different than those in the smear preparation. They appear as discs with sharp contours which often look like empty rings (ghost cells) (Fig. 71).

Casts

Casts often indicate kidney damage. They are oval, cylindrical particles. The beginner often accidentally confuses contaminants in the urine with casts, so it is advisable to be careful in evaluating the structures.

Hyaline casts appear almost transparent, delicate, and without inclusions. They are difficult to find and easy to overlook, especially if they occur only in small numbers. To look for hyaline casts, work with the condenser diaphragm as narrow as possible—these structures are indistinct if the illumination is too strong.

Granular casts are easier to find. Fine or coarse granulation can be seen on the inside.

Just as with hyaline casts, waxy casts reveal no special internal structures. They are formed as discharges from pathologically enlarged renal tubules and are therefore wider than the other casts. They are characterized by a dull gloss quite similar to that of wax. Their edges often show deep notches.

Epithelial casts consist of columnar epithelial cells which have been pressed together. Usually the cells which make up an epithelial cast are in the process of degeneration, and sometimes scarcely more than the outlines of the individual cells can be seen.

White-blood-cell casts consist of white blood corpuscles or of casts of other types embedded in the white blood corpuscles. These casts are not often found. Their occurrence may indicate an inflammation of the kidneys.

Red-blood-cell casts consist of red blood corpuscles.

Fatty casts develop from the accumulation of innumerable droplets of fat. They are also very rare. Droplets of fat can be recognized in the microscopic preparation by their bright lustre. In doubtful cases, the droplet of fat can be studied simply by using a drop of milk for comparison.

As for other casts, properly speaking, all of the constituents which occur in urine can appear associated in the cylindrical form. Therefore, a careful study is absolutely necessary to determine which types of casts are present.

Crystals in Urine Sediment

In many sediments you will find different kinds of crystals. Their presence does not usually mean much. Only certain kinds of crystals or large numbers of them can be considered as a serious symptom.

Urates are light or dark brown amorphous (noncrystalline) granules in mosslike arrangements which are visible under low-power magnification. They occur even in urine from healthy people—under certain circumstances, in enormous quantities. Urates dissolve just by warming. Often a thick rusty or yellowish precipitate can be seen with the naked eye (uric acid crystals) in urine which has been put in a cool place, especially during winter. This so-called brick dust sediment merely consists of very small granules which have no special crystalline structure.

Crystals of calcium oxalate are also a very frequent constituent of urine. They look like small envelopes and can be recognized immediately from this characteristic shape. They are insoluble in acetic acid, but dissolve in strong hydrochloric acid.

Uric acid crystals can occur in so many forms that they are difficult to describe. They occur in the shape of whetstones, rhombic plates, isolated and fused rods, and many other forms. Uric acid crystals are insoluble in acetic and hydrochloric acids, but dissolve readily in sodium or potassium hydroxide.

Xanthine also occurs in the shape of whetstone crystals. To distinguish one from the other, note that xanthine has little or no coloration, whereas uric acid crystals often appear yellow-red-brownish. Moreover, xanthine is somewhat soluble in hydrochloric acid.

Because of their typical shape, crystals of ammonium magnesium phosphate are also called coffin-lid crystals. They are soluble in acetic acid.

Cystine appears as hexagonal plates. It does not dissolve in acetic acid, but is readily soluble in hydrochloric acid and in potassium and sodium hydroxides. Cystine in the urine indicates disturbances in the protein metabolism.

Leucine forms irregular or smooth spheres, often with cracklike streaks.

It is slightly soluble in acetic acid, and readily soluble in hydrochloric acid and potassium and sodium hydroxides.

Tyrosine appears in the form of fine needles which can occur singly, but are often associated together in bundles.

Leucine and tyrosine do not normally occur in the urine. Their presence may indicate liver damage.

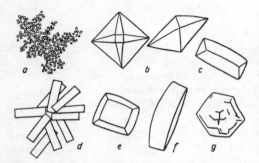

Fig. 72. Various crystals which can often be found in urine sediment. a=urate (brick dust); b=calcium oxalate (envelope crystals); c= ammonium magnesium phosphate (coffin-lid crystal); d, e, and f=uric acid (f= whetstone form); g=cystine.

Contaminants in Urine Sediment

It should be understood that in every microscopic study contamination can lead to errors. Numerous contaminants are present particularly in urine sediment; the most frequent of these will be mentioned here.

Starch granules rank among the most common contaminants. Among other things, they can come from preserving containers which have not been well cleaned, or they can fall from the air into urine which has been left standing open. Detect with the iodine reaction (Lugol's solution, p. 8).

Pollen is also frequently found in urine sediments, especially in spring.

Textile fibres can come from the cloth with which the microscope slide was cleaned. (See Chapter 9 on Textile Fibres.)

Yeast cells and fungal hyphae are often found in urine which has stood for some time. Under certain circumstances, they find a good culture medium here and multiply correspondingly. (See Chapter 11 on Bacteria and Fungi.) Yeast cells often overgrow all other constituents, especially in urines containing sugar. Consequently, in all determinations of sugar in the urine, especially in quantitative investigations, results obtained from fermenting urine samples must be evaluated carefully. The beginner is advised to look at both yeast cells and red blood corpuscles closely before passing judgment on a urine sediment, since mix-ups are not inconceivable.

Sperm often occur in urine sediment. They are dead and motionless, but the structure of the head and tail parts can still be clearly recognized.

Droplets of fat, if they actually come from the urine, are a pathological constituent of the sediment. However, they are usually result from microscope slides or other equipment not being well cleaned.

Bacteria are found in almost every urine sediment. If they do occur, it can be important to determine whether they come from the urinary tract or are only to be considered as contaminants. Catheterized urine, which must be taken by a physician, is used to solve this problem correctly. Large numbers of bacteria occur in urine which has stood for a long time, especially during warm weather. They multiply well here, especially if the urine is alkaline.

Preserving Urine Samples and Making Permanent Preparations

Occasionally it is necessary to keep urine samples for relatively long periods of time. Urine can be preserved with toluene for shorter periods. Enough toluene is added so that a thin layer of toluene still remains on the surface after thorough shaking. If it is necessary to preserve the cells in urine especially well, preservation with formalin is recommended, since urine preserved with formalin is stable almost indefinitely. Dilute a 40% formalin solution with urine in a 1:10 to a 1:20 ratio. However, only the organized constituents remain safely unchanged.

Permanent preparations can be made with glycerine jelly as a mounting medium. A drop of glycerine jelly of the same size or slightly larger is added to urine sediment on a microscope slide. It is mixed well and covered with a cover-glass. After the jelly stiffens, a tightly-fitting ring of lacquer must be drawn around it. It is better to mount in glycerine jelly between two cover-glasses and to seal with a synthetic mounting medium. (See p. 34 for a more detailed description of this method.)

8. Examining Stools

Studying stools is so interesting that every microscopist should overcome his understandable aversion and look at a stool sample under the microscope. Even nonpathological stools are instructive in showing which constituents of food are assimilated and which are indigestible waste matter. In case of a diet rich in plants, you will be surprised at the large amount of plant residues excreted without being digested. The human body has no enzyme capable of dissolving the substance in the cell walls of plants (cellulose). The extent to which cellulose is nevertheless attacked is due to bacteria which are present in tremendous numbers in the intestine. Among these bacteria are species which can hydrolyze (split) cellulose into fatty acids and sugars.

With the help of bacteria, at least a small portion of the cellulose is made available to the body. This is an impressive example of the great importance of the intestinal flora, which consist largely of bacteria. In addition, the microscopist interested in botany will be delighted with the excellent macerated preparations of plant cells and tissue to be found in the stool. Especially if the stool has been subjected to the method employed for concentrating worm eggs, remarkably skeletonized vessels will be found in which the fine structures can be studied better than in any other macerated preparations.

It hardly needs to be emphasized that in studying stools you must work very neatly. However, neat work will have become a matter of course to the experienced microscopist so that he can be entrusted to study stools.

Examining stools is dangerous because they may turn out to be pathological, and it seems wise to add a further word of caution here, perhaps directing the student to slides of parasites from stools which are available from biological supply houses, as a substitute for the procedures given here.

DETECTION OF FOOD RESIDUES IN THE STOOL

Take several pieces about the size of peas from a stool sample and stir them with water to the consistency of a thin paste. Under some circumstances, watery stools can be studied without dilution.

Find a mass of the smallest particles with low-power magnification. This mass, the detritus, consists of decomposed parts of food which no longer have a particularly recognizable structure and, especially, of vast numbers of bacteria. At many spots, larger constituents reveal clearly seen structures. Plant residues can be recognized immediately as such by the typical structure of the plant cells. Now and again you will find muscle fibres when meat has been eaten; their transverse striation can usually be seen clearly, and they can be identified without difficulty by this. You will also readily recognize residues from connective tissue by their fibrous structure.

If you study stools from human beings who have eaten different kinds of food, you will soon find that the composition of the stool varies within wide limits according to the diet. This fact is important in passing judgment on pathological stools. For example, the appearance of accumulated muscle-fibre fragments indicates digestive disturbances and, under certain circumstances, even pancreatic insufficiency. However, if the diet contained excessive amounts of meat it would be quite normal to find large quantities of muscle fibres, since the intestine and the digestive enzymes it secretes are able to digest only a certain portion of the food offered to it; the rest is excreted unused. Because of this, a standardized test diet is often given so that food residues in the stool can be evaluated with certainty, for it is then known exactly which residues will occur in non-pathological stools. For example, in the test diet specified by Schmidt and Strasburger the following foods are supplied for 2 to 3 days divided into 5 meals per day (cited from Hallmann):

1.5 litres of milk; 100 gms. rusks; 2 eggs; 50 gms. butter; 125 gms. lean beef; 190 gms. potatoes; and 80 gms. cooked oatmeal.

The stool examination is performed only after this test diet has been administered for 2 to 3 days. However, with some experience and, above all, with some information on the foods eaten previously, the stool can be evaluated quite well, even without a test diet. It is often advisable not only to examine stools by the simple methods described here, but also to employ the technique for concentrating worm eggs described below even when studying foods. This technique concentrates the heavier components, while the lighter particles which occasionally interfere are removed.

Muscle fibres from meat also occur here and there in the stools of healthy human beings. However, large amounts of muscle fibres suggest the presence of digestive disturbances, especially after a test diet is administered. These disturbances can sometimes be directly related to an absence or insufficiency of enzymatic action. You know, of course, that the digestion of proteins is carried out in the intestine by proteolytic (protein-splitting) enzymes from the pancreas. If there is interference with the action of these enzymes, the muscle fibres cannot be digested and assimilated, since proteolytic enzymes from the stomach and the intestinal wall are not sufficient to digest them. In other cases, inadequate digestion of proteins can be caused indirectly by interference with the secretion of bile. The bile acids are indispensable for assimilation of fatlike substances by the intestine. If they are absent, fatty acids remain in the intestine and can cover proteins which have not yet been digested. This protective covering by fatty acids largely prevents the attack of trypsin, a proteolytic enzyme from the pancreas. In almost every case it is easy to decide whether an abnormal accumulation of muscle fibres in the stool results from a direct interference with the enzyme action or from the exclusion of bile from the intestine. In the case of diseases which prevent the adequate secretion of bile, there are many other symptoms including the presence of large amounts of fat in the stool. But the simultaneous appearance of large quantities of muscle fibres and fat cannot always be traced back to a deficiency of bile acids. Both the proteolytic and lipolytic (fat-splitting) enzyme actions of the pancreas can be impaired.

Muscle fibres in the stool usually still display their characteristic transverse striation. Naturally, the stool never contains entire fibres, but only small fragments. When you have greatly swollen, partially digested muscle fibres, carry out a protein reaction for confirmation: Mix a small amount of the stool sample on a microscope slide with a large drop of nitric acid and heat it. Proteins turn yellow.

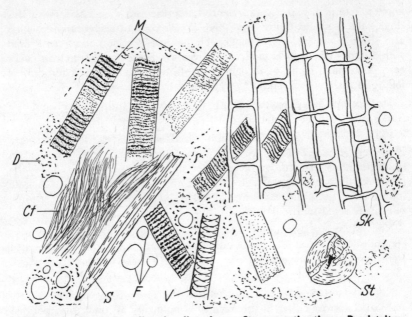

Fig. 73. Stool sediment in a digestive disturbance. Ct=connective tissue; D=detritus; F=fat droplets; V=spiral vessel from vegetable food; M=particles of muscle fibre; Sk=cell skeleton from vegetable food; S=sclerenchyma fibre from vegetable food; St=corroded starch granule.

Fibrous connective tissue can also be recognized at a glance in stool samples by its fibrous structure. Cohering, fibrous, often slimy masses frequently consist of connective tissue which can be seen even with the naked eye. Wash them in water and examine them under the microscope. In doubtful cases, add some 10% acetic acid to the preparation. If it really is connective tissue, the fibrous structure will swell up.

It is quite normal to find connective tissue in the stool. However, if it appears after a test diet has been administered, it may often be traced back to digestive disturbances in the stomach.

If starch occurs only in small amounts in the stool, it should not be considered pathological. However, larger amounts of starch, especially pasty starch, suggest that there are disturbances in the digestion of starch. After administering a test diet, pasty starch should not occur at all. You know that a starch granule can frequently be recognized by its characteristic arrangement in rings. In most cases, however, starch granules found in the stool have lost this arrangement in rings so that you have to depend on other characteristics. The external form of the starch granule is often retained, and the experienced microscopist can make use of this single fact as a clue. Quite often there are corroded starch granules which also show a characteristic image. The iodine reaction, best performed with Lugol's solution, is used to confirm the presence of starch in every case. You have come to recognize the blue of starch after addition of iodine in the study of foods.

Pasty starch is a glassy, swollen mass. As a rule, individual granules of starch can no longer be found in it.

Fatlike substances are found in normal stools in the form of soaps. However, after test diets have been administered, fats are only present in small amounts. A considerable increase of fats in the stool indicates the presence of disturbances which can be different in origin. These include interference with the excretion of bile and inhibition of the enzyme system excreted by the pancreas.

Neutral fat is a compound of fatty acids with glycerine. The substances commonly known as fats are usually neutral fats. Fatty acids are formed from neutral fats, for example, by the action of enzymes (lipases) which split off the glycerine. Soaps are the alkali salts of fatty acids.

Neutral fats are found in the stool in the form of fat droplets. Fatty acids also appear either in the form of droplets or as long, thin, pointed needles. Soaps appear as needles or in clumps with a variety of forms.

Use the following methods to distinguish between fatty acids and neutral fats on the one hand and soaps on the other: Heat the stool sample rather intensely on a microscope slide. Neutral fats and fatty acids melt and assume the droplet form, while soaps remain unmelted for the time being. Under certain circumstances the fatty acids return to their former state (needles or globules) when they cool.

Now add a fairly strong solution of acetic acid (about 30%) to a second stool sample and heat again until the sample begins to boil. During this process the fatty acids will be liberated from the soaps and will concentrate as droplets of fatty acid. Naturally, neutral fats and fatty acids which were originally present will also change into the form of droplets. Since even the soaps exist as fatty acids after the combined use of acetic acid and heat, you can now stain all of the fat which is present with Sudan III. Without this preliminary treatment the soaps would not stain with Sudan. Use the following Sudan solution (quoted from Hallmann):

> 96% alcohol......................10 cc.
> 30% acetic acid..................90 cc.
> Sudan III........................ 0.2 gm.

Mix several drops of this solution well with the stool sample on the slide and heat the preparation. Fatty substances appear to be stained red, orange, or brownish-red.

DETECTION OF BLOOD IN THE STOOL

The detection of blood has such great practical importance that we will discuss it here, although it is not usually carried out with a microscope.

Blood cannot always be seen in the stool with the naked eye. The detection of hidden (occult) blood is therefore extremely important, but a few precautionary rules must be followed to avoid errors in judgment. Meat contains haemoglobin and therefore should not be eaten for at least 3 days before the study. Chlorophyll can also interfere with the reaction. Consequently, plant food rich in chlorophyll should also be avoided as much as possible. Besides this, other haemorrhages not originating in the intestine must be considered (haemorrhoids and even harmless bleeding in the mucous membrane of the mouth).

Immediately before the examination, dissolve some benzidine in a few cc. of glacial acetic acid. Use just enough benzidine so that a few granules remain undissolved. Add an equal volume of 3% hydrogen peroxide to this benzidine solution. Mix the stool sample with 4 times its weight in water and heat just to the boiling point. Now pour the diluted stool sample drop by drop into the benzidine solution. If blood is present, a blue or greenish-blue develops.

DETECTION OF PARASITES IN THE STOOL

Of the many intestinal parasites found in the stool, chiefly those animals which are classified as "worms" will be considered here. There are also many intestinal parasites among the unicellular animals, but the very dangerous types are rare in a temperate climate. Besides, they usually need to be examined by a specialist.

If whole worms or at least parts of them are found in the stool, the only problem still remaining is to identify the species present. This is usually easy to do. It is much more difficult to detect an invasion of worms if the suspicion can only be confirmed by finding worm eggs in the stool.

Worm eggs can be located either in the direct preparation or after concentration. The latter method is much more reliable than the direct examination of a stool suspension.

To examine a stool without concentrating it, take samples from a stool at several points and stir them with a little water into a paste which is not too thin. Make several preparations from this and inspect them all carefully, one after the other.

To concentrate worm eggs, take several stool samples the size of peas at various points distant from one another and triturate them with water until a pasty consistency is obtained. (With watery stools dilution with water is obviously unnecessary.) Now place the paste in a large test tube, add the same volume of 25% hydrochloric acid, and twice this volume of ether (for example, 5 cc. stool, 5 cc. hydrochloric acid, and 10 cc. ether). Close the test tube with a tight-fitting cork and then shake it well. Since ether vapours could cause the tube to explode when shaken, remove the cork from time to time and then replace it. When the contents of the test tube are quite uniformly mixed, filter them into a centrifuge tube through 2 or 3 layers of surgical gauze stretched over a glass funnel. During the centrifugation which follows, several layers are formed in the centrifuge tube, along with a plug of solid material. Loosen this plug carefully from the wall of the tube with a glass rod, and pour out the entire contents except the sediment. Examine the sediment for worm eggs under the microscope.

Roundworms or Threadworms (Nematodes)

A nematode which is justifiably feared is the eelworm or roundworm, *Ascaris lumbricoides*. According to Bergstermann, Mendheim, and Scheid, a female roundworm produces 200,000 eggs a day. The total egg count of one female is 27,000,000. Roundworm eggs excreted with the stool are not immediately capable of producing infection again. They must first pass through a process of incubation, the length of which varies from 10 to 40 days, depending upon the temperature and other environmental conditions. The eggs remain viable for a long time and can still infect new hosts years later. The chief sources of infection are vegetables which have been fertilized with human dung.

If roundworm eggs (which already contain larvae) capable of producing infection reach the intestine of a human being, the larvae are freed and bore through the intestinal wall into the lymphatic and blood vessels, finally reaching the lungs through the blood stream. From here they rise to the larynx, are then swallowed, and grow to sexual maturity in the intestine. Eggs of roundworms are relatively easy to find in the stool, especially if they have been concentrated. They are oval, 45 to 75μ long and 35 to 50μ wide. The thick eggshell is covered with a brown albuminoid coat which is scalloped. Roundworm eggs can be recognized at first glance by this albuminoid layer (Fig. 74).

The common pinworm, *Enterobius vermicularis* (*Oxyuris vermicularis*) is so widespread that almost every human being has come into contact with it at least once. The adult females migrate from the intestine or are evacuated with the stool. The female prefers to lay her eggs in the anal region, where she can cause severe itching by her wandering back and forth. The eggs can get on the hands and under the fingernails by scratching, making self-infection entirely possible.

Pinworm eggs occur only rarely in the stool or urine and are found there only accidentally. An anal swab must be made to confirm the presence of pinworm eggs. Wipe the area surrounding the anus with a moist wad of cotton. Then take some material from the immediate vicinity of the anus with a wooden spatula, or press cellophane tape firmly on the sphincter muscle. In the first case, mix the material on the microscope slide with a 0.5% solution of sodium hydroxide and then examine it under the microscope; in the second case, examine the cellophane tape under the microscope directly.

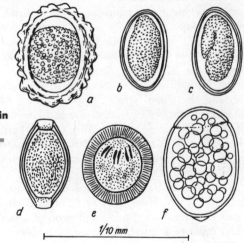

Fig. 74. Especially important worm eggs which can be found in stool. a=roundworm (Ascaris); b and c=common pinworm; d= whipworm; e=beef tapeworm; f=fish tapeworm.

1/10 mm

Pinworm eggs have a very characteristic shape. They are asymetrical. One long side of the otherwise oval and smooth egg is more convex than the other. They are 50 to 60μ long and about 20 to 30μ wide (Fig. 74).

The whipworm, *Trichuris trichiura*, is a common worm 3 to 5 cm. long. Whipworms also have a certain period of incubation until they become capable of infection again. This incubation lasts 14 days to one year, depending upon environmental conditions.

The shape of the egg is typical, but the eggs are not easy to find. Therefore, it is advisable to use the concentration technique when looking for whipworm eggs. The eggs are definitely lemon-shaped and have a light spot or polar plug at each end. They are 50 to 55μ long and 22 to 25μ wide (Fig. 74).

The other nematodes which attack humans (among them some very dangerous species) are fortunately so rare that they may be omitted here.

Tapeworms

Tapeworms are adapted to parasitism to an extreme degree. They have no intestine and consequently absorb their food through the surface of their body. Most tapeworms have a characteristic segmentation: many segments (proglottides), which are delicate and thin near the head are connected with a head (scolex). The segments become larger and broader at increasing distances from the head. Everyone knows about the typical flattening of tapeworm segments. How does the remarkable structure of this animal come about?

New segments are continually formed behind the head. The segments just developing naturally push to the rear the ones previously formed. In this way, a whole chain of such segments develops and it can often be many metres long. To a certain extent each segment is an animal in itself. That is, in every segment there is a complete male and female sexual apparatus (most tapeworms are hermaphrodites). The segments forming the chain (strobila) are gravid (full of eggs). They contain an enormous number of fertilized eggs in a canal called the uterus. In two of our most common tapeworms, the beef tapeworm (*Taenia saginata*) and the pork tapeworm (*Taenia solium*), the mature segments are shed as a whole. The eggs, which already contain embryos, are freed by the disintegration of the segments.

The head of the tapeworm is anchored to the intestinal mucosa with hooklets or cup-shaped suckers, or with both. The head's structure is often important for the identification of a tapeworm. For this reason, the head must be located, occasionally by lengthy searching.

By far the greatest number of tapeworms change hosts. That is, not all stages of the parasite's development inhabit the same host. The eggs containing embryos reach an intermediate host. In this host the embryos are freed from the embryonal covering (the egg), they bore through the intestinal mucosa, and reach the muscles through the blood vessels. There they form a sac in which the head of the young tapeworm develops. Under conditions suitable for the tapeworm, these bladderlike cysts (cysticerci) are transferred to the final host when it eats the meat of the intermediate host. The cysticerci are disintegrated in the gastro-intestinal tract of the final host, the head is freed, becomes established in the intestinal mucosa, and new tapeworm segments begin to form immediately.

Especially dangerous are tapeworms for which man is not the final host, but the intermediate host. The cysticerci can cause severe illness if they are formed in vital organs. For example, the dog tapeworm (*Echinococcus granulosus*), for which man serves as the intermediate host, can even kill humans infested with this parasite.

The beef tapeworm (*Taenia saginata*) is probably the tapeworm which occurs most frequently in man. The chief intermediate hosts are cattle. Man becomes infested by eating incompletely cooked or raw beef with cysticerci. The beef tapeworm can grow to extreme length. It is usually between 5 and 10 metres long, but some considerably longer specimens have also been found. The head has 4 cup-shaped suckers, but no crown of hooklets.

Eggs (true embryos) and segments of the beef tapeworm are found in the stool. The eggs are surrounded by a tough, radially streaked embryonal sac which allows you to recognize them readily (Fig. 74).

In crushed preparations the mature segments of the beef tapeworm display a characteristic structure. The uterus, containing fertilized eggs, has a dead-end which makes it impossible for the eggs to get out. Originally a straight tube, the uterus may now contain numerous caecal-like protrusions because of the enormous number of eggs which have accumulated in it. In their turn, these protrusions can be branched. Segments of the beef tapeworm can be distinguished from those of the pork tapeworm relatively easily by these protrusions of the uterus; although such protrusions of the uterus are also present in the pork tapeworm, they are much thinner, more subdivided, and more numerous in the beef tapeworm (Fig. 75).

Branchings from the uterus cannot always be recognized clearly enough. In such cases, you can try using stained preparation to achieve your goal.

Place the segments to be studied in 70% alcohol for 1 to 2 days and then transfer them into a borax-carmine solution (see p. 24), leaving them there until they are stained all the way through. (This can take several days.) Finally, differentiation is carried out in hydrochloric acid and alcohol until the objects no longer give off stain (2 to 48 hours). After differentiation wash them well in 70% alcohol, and finally transfer them from 90% and 100% alcohol into xylene. When the tapeworm segments have become quite transparent in xylene, mount them in some synthetic mounting medium after lining the cover-glass with fragments from a microscope slide.

Segments and heads of tapeworms must sometimes be sought in the stool. For this purpose, a large stool sample is suspended in water, allowed to settle, and the supernatant water is decanted. Repeat this process until the water remains relatively clear when the sediment is suspended. Then examine the sediment carefully.

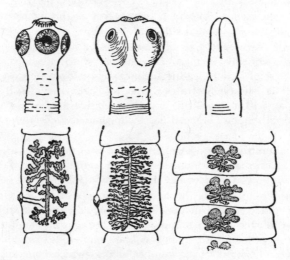

Fig. 75. Heads and gravid segments of the pork tapeworm (left), beef tapeworm (middle), and fish tapeworm (right).

(Adapted from Kükenthal
Mattes, *Leitfaden für das
zoologische Praktikum*, Gustav
Fischer Verlag, Stuttgart, 1943.)

The pork tapeworm (*Taenia solium*) has become rare. This has happened especially because the cysticerci of the pork tapeworm are often present in large numbers and are therefore not so easy to overlook in the inspection of meat. The pork tapeworm is more dangerous than the beef tapeworm, especially because man can serve as both a final and intermediate host.

The eggs of the pork tapeworm closely resemble those of the beef tapeworm. However, the heads and segments of the pork and beef tapeworms can be distinguished from one another immediately. The head of the beef tapeworm has 4 cup-shaped suckers, while that of the pork tapeworm has, in addition, 2 crowns of hooklets. In the mature segments of the pork tapeworm, the uterus also has characteristic protrusions, but these are much heavier and less numerous than in the beef tapeworm (Fig. 75).

The fish tapeworm (*Diphyllobothrium latum*) is extremely rare. It differs from the two tapeworms just described both in its life cycle and structure. First of all, it is interesting that the fish tapeworm needs not just one, but two, intermediate hosts for its development. The embryo must reach water and be eaten there by a copepod (minute crustacean found in fresh or salt water). The first larval stage, the procercoid, develops in the gastric cavity of the copepod. If the copepod is eaten by a fish, a second larval stage, the plerocercoid, develops in the fish's musculature. The tapeworm can develop completely only if the fish is eaten by the final host in a raw, smoked, or underdone condition. In areas where fish is eaten raw, man is often the final host of this parasite.

The head of the fish tapeworm is narrow, has two sucking grooves (sulci), and is usually described as spatulate or almond-shaped.

Anatomically, the segments of the fish tapeworm differ considerably from those of the beef or the pork tapeworm. Above all, the sexual apparatus of the fish tapeworm contains a vitellarium which produces yolk cells (vitelline material) as a food substance for the egg. In addition, the uterus in the fish tapeworm does not have a dead-end, but has an opening leading outside. The presence of yolk cells calls for a special type of egg. Unlike the uteri of the tapeworms, the uterus which opens to the outside does not need to protrude as much, since the eggs are released gradually.

The eggs of the fish tapeworm are oval in shape, have an operculum (a lid or covering structure) at the upper pole, and contain both the embryo and the yolk material. They are about 70μ long and about 45μ wide. Segments of the fish tapeworm can be recognized by the rosette-shaped uterus (Figs. 74 and 75).

Although the dog tapeworm (*Echinococcus granulosus*) cannot be taken into consideration during examination of the stool, it should at least be mentioned again here in passing because of its great danger. The worm is very small. The chain consists of only 3 to 4 segments. Final hosts are the dog, wolf, and fox, while various domestic animals as well as man are possible intermediate hosts. In the intermediate host, the larvae prefer to establish themselves in the liver and to form cysticerci here which can enlarge greatly because of their budding. *Echinococcus* cysticerci can become as large as an apple or even as large as a child's head. Human infestation generally occurs by contact with infested dogs (petting, hand-licking, and so forth). Because of this, children in particular should be urged to wash their hands if they have played with infected dogs.

9. Studying Textile Fibres

The microscope plays an important role in the practical work of recognizing and identifying textile fibres. In hardly a single instance are the numerous macroscopic tests (chemical examination, burning, feel, etc.) adequate for making completely positive identification.

For the most part, textile microscopists are experienced specialists, able to ascertain not only the type of fibre, but also its origin. Besides this, they can often make important statements about the quality and working up of the fibres being examined.

Obviously, in the scope of this book you will be able to get only a condensed over-all view of the technique for examining fibres. You can safely leave it to the expert to establish whether a cotton comes from Egypt or America or whether a flax was subjected to normal or artificially accelerated retting. You will be dealing with what is really in the suit or the tie you just bought. For this you need no specialized knowledge but only a little experience and—if at all possible—a useful collection of comparative preparations.

Modern technology recognizes an enormous number of fibres, all of which can be used for the purposes of the textile industry in one way or another. Only the fibres most commonly used at present will be discussed here. In general, you can distinguish between three large groups of textile fibres:

1. NATURAL FIBRES: Vegetable fibres such as cotton, hemp, and flax belong in this category together with the animal fibres, wool and silk. In spite of the surprisingly rapid development of artificial fibres, natural fibres still play the most important role at the present time.

2. SEMI-SYNTHETIC FIBRES: To this category belong, for example, the staple fibres (rayon staples) and artificial silks. The initial raw materials for semisynthetic fibres are products of plant, or in a few cases also of

animal, origin. They are put into solution, drawn out into fine threads, and solidified again in this form.

3. SYNTHETIC FIBRES: Examples of synthetic fibres are nylon, perlon, and orlon. A great future has been predicted for synthetic fibres, but at the present time we cannot judge to what extent they will replace natural fibres.

The technique of examining fibres is simple. In most cases, it is sufficient to observe the fibres in glycerine or a mixture of glycerine and alcohol. Along with this, it is sometimes advisable to mount them in a medium with a low refractive index, e.g., water, and in a medium with a higher refractive index, e.g., Canada balsam or a synthetic mounting medium, such as Permount. In some cases simple microchemical reactions are necessary. The most important of these are:

Reaction for cellulose: Cellulose is dyed a violet-blue in a solution of zinc chloride and iodine and dissolves in ammonia containing copper hydroxide (cuprammonium or Schweitzer's reagent).

Reaction for lignin: Lignin is stained red in a solution of phloroglucinol and hydrochloric acid.

Reaction for natural silk: Silk dissolves in an alkaline solution of copper and glycerine.

Reaction for acetate fibres: Acetate fibres dissolve in acetone, leaving thin membranes behind.

For preparation of the reagents, see p. 169.

It has already been mentioned that examining fibres can be made easier by as complete a collection of comparative preparations as possible. Therefore, you should make permanent preparations from known material which is completely pure. Although dyed preparations may be mounted in a synthetic mounting medium, Canada balsam, or something similar, it is more advisable to use undyed preparations in a solution of glycerine and gelatine. (See p. 34.) In comparative observations it is important that only fibres mounted in the same medium be compared with one another. The material to be studied must consequently be observed in the same mounting medium as used for making the preparation with which it is to be compared.

Usually, longitudinal views of the fibres are examined. Occasionally, however, you must also look at cross-sections. To prepare cross-sections, first pierce a cork with a fine sewing-machine needle which has been threaded. Hold the loop of thread as it comes out on the other side, and draw the needle out again. Place the bundle of fibres in the loop and draw it into the cork along with the thread. Using a straight razor, cut off the thinnest slices of cork possible; these will contain cross-sections of the fibres at the point where they were drawn into the cork. Your collection of comparative preparations should also contain cross-sections of the more important and common fibres.

NATURAL FIBRES

Wool

Place a little wool in a drop of glycerine on a microscope slide and isolate a few individual fibres with two dissecting needles. Place a cover-glass on top, and examine first with low-power magnification, then with medium-power. Your attention will be attracted, even at first glance, by the strange scale structure of the fibres. The individual scales covering the surface overlap like the tiles on a roof. Because of their scale structure, wool fibres look notched at the edges (Fig. 76).

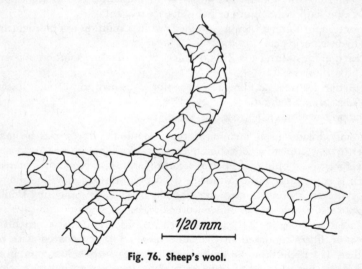

1/20 mm

Fig. 76. Sheep's wool.

Like all hair from mammals, wool fibres consist of keratin. You can distinguish between the medulla (central portion) which cannot be seen in finer wools, the cortex, and the cuticle. The latter, consisting of a layer of flat, completely horned, dead cells, causes the conspicuous scale structure by which you can identify wool fibres at first glance. Naturally, the hair of other mammals is quite similar in structure to that of sheep, but since mixtures of sheep wool with other animal hairs can be detected only by experts, it is not necessary to go into it in more detail here.

In textile products you will often find reprocessed wool, i.e., wool which has already been used once. Reprocessed wool is often inferior in quality. With the microscope you can distinguish reprocessed wool quite easily from other wool. In reprocessed wool, the ends of separate fibres are often not cut off smoothly or uniformly rounded, but are pulled out in tufts. Besides this, reprocessed wool is often so badly damaged that the scale structure can no longer be seen at all. In this case, you must use the notched edge for identification, because it occurs in this form only in animal hairs.

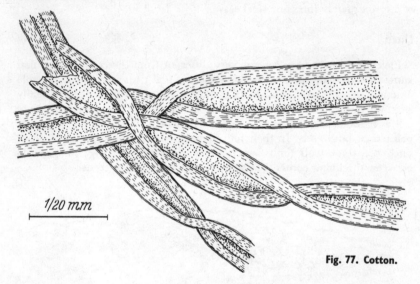

1/20 mm

Fig. 77. Cotton.

Cotton

The only vegetable hairs used in the textile industry are the hull fibres of *Gossypium*, which come on the market as cotton. As even superficial examination shows, they are one-celled hairs. In a glycerine preparation you can see the thick cell walls and the cell cavity (lumen) clearly. The cotton fibre consists of almost pure cellulose. In a solution of zinc chloride and iodine the cell walls are stained an intense violet, in cuprammonium they dissolve with characteristic swelling, and reactions for lignin are negative.

Since cotton fibres are an epidermal structure, the thin outer membrane or cuticle, consisting of a wax-like substance, can be seen on careful examination.

The most important characteristic of cotton is that the individual fibres are twisted in many places. Such twists do occur occasionally in other fibres, but never so regularly and so often as in cotton. Cotton can be distinguished from all other fibres with some certainty by this characteristic alone (Fig. 77). However, cotton can be mechanically treated in such a way that the twists disappear and both the fibres and cloth shine. This mercerized cotton can be distinguished under the microscope from rayon staple by the fact that it does not swell in water. Two preparations, one in a solution of glycerine and alcohol and one in water, must show fibres of approximately the same thickness.

Linen

Flax fibre comes from a tissue very different from the cotton fibre. You know that in many plants there is a mechanical tissue which has the sole function of supporting the plant. Consequently, its cells are especially resistant to mechanical strains. Phloem or bast fibres are a special type of cell in this mechanical tissue. These are long cells with thick walls, usually pointed at both ends. In their fully developed state these cells are dead, since the thick wall limits much too greatly an exchange of material between the living contents of the cell and the adjacent cells.

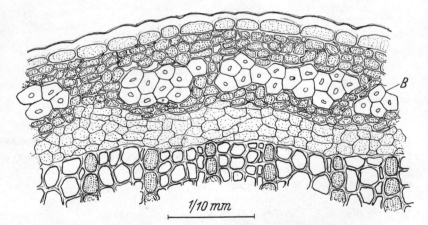

1/10 mm

Fig. 78. Cross-section through the edge of a stalk of flax. B= bast fibres.

In order to obtain a general view of the pattern and shape of these bast fibres, first prepare a cross-section of a stalk of flax (Fig. 78). In the outer layers of the stalk, in the basic tissue composed of delicate, living cells, you will find bundles of thick-walled, often angular cells with narrow cell cavities—the bast fibres of flax. A longitudinal section or macerated preparation (see p. 82) will then give you more exact information about the shape of these cells.

Bast fibres in the plant body withstand great exposure to stress. Just think of what wind pressure such a thin stalk of flax can be exposed to! The valuable mechanical properties of these cells can be utilized by man. These bast fibres are removed from the tissue and converted into textile fabrics.

The bundle of bast fibres is dissolved from the flax stalk by means of retting. In flax retting, man has been acting as a bacteriologist for centuries—without knowing it!

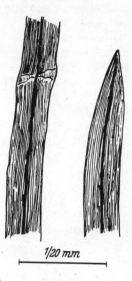

Fig. 79. Flax fibres; lumen drawn in black.

1/20 mm

You are already acquainted with the central lamella, the delicate membrane which connects the cell walls of adjacent cells with one another. This central lamella consists of pectin substances. If they dissolve, then the cells naturally separate. There are certain micro-organisms, particularly bacteria, which have an enzyme (pectinase) which decomposes and dissolves the pectin substances. In flax retting, the stalks are subjected to the action of pectin-destroying micro-organisms by placing them in water (water retting) or by laying them out on a field (dew retting). It is a special art to begin flax retting properly and to interrupt it at the right time, for only the bundles of bast fibres should be

159

separated from the tissue structure, not the individual bast cells. If retting is carried too far, there is the danger that the structure of the bast fibre bundle will also be attacked. After retting, the bundle of fibres can be removed relatively easily from the stalk by mechanical means (scutching).

You must realize that the textile industry treats the entire bundle of fibres and consequently calls the fibre bundle a fibre. For your examinations, however, you cannot use the fibre bundle, for it is much too thick for microscopic observation. You must examine the individual cells and isolate them beforehand from the structure of the bundle.

Take a sample of flax and reduce several bundles to fibres with thin needles in glycerine on the microscope slide. You must unravel it to the extent that separate cells are actually present. Unravelling is tedious work. Often the individual cells may be separated more easily if a bundle of fibres is passed repeatedly between two fingernails pressed firmly together. It is not advisable to separate the cells by chemical methods, as is often recommended (e.g., by boiling in nitric acid), since the fibres can become somewhat changed in this way.

Under the microscope you will see that the individual bast fibres in flax have thick walls and a strikingly narrow cellular cavity which looks like a line, even under high-power magnification. The ends are sharply pointed in general (Fig. 79). Bast fibres often appear to be angular in cross-section, or more rarely, rounded (Fig. 80). The great length of a single bast cell is interesting. Tobler-Wolff reports a length of 2–4 cm.

Fig. 80. Flax fibres; cross-section.

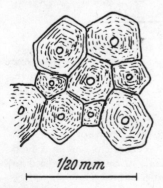

1/20 mm

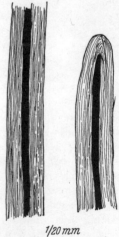

1/20 mm

Fig. 81. Hemp; lumen drawn in black.

160

If you examine flax fibres in a solution of zinc chloride and iodine, they will soon turn an intense violet. On the other hand, you will wait in vain for a red in phloroglucinol and hydrochloric acid. Therefore, flax fibre consists of cellulose and is not lignified. Accordingly, it dissolves in cuprammonium.

Hemp

Just like the industrial flax fibre, the industrial hemp fibre consists of bundles of bast fibres. In examining hemp you must also divide such a bundle of fibres into its individual cells.

Even the first glance into the microscope shows that the hemp fibre is very much like flax fibre. It requires a great deal of practice to be able to distinguish between flax and hemp, and from time to time even seasoned experts sometimes cannot come to a definite decision.

Fig. 82. Hemp fibres; cross-section.

1/20 mm

The lumen (the cell cavity) of the bast fibre from hemp is often considerably wider than that of the bast fibre from flax (Fig. 81). In cross-section, the individual fibres appear to be more rounded than in flax (Fig. 82), and the ends of the fibre are usually not so pointed as in flax, but appear rounder. Hemp does not turn quite as intense a violet with zinc chloride and iodine as does flax. If cross-sections of hemp fibres are placed in zinc chloride and iodine, the outer side often displays yellow lines.

Jute

Jute consists of bast fibres from the plant, *Corchorus*, which occurs in India. If you examine an unravelled bundle of fibres, you will find that

161

the lumen is not uniformly thick. The cell walls approach one another and recede again at rather regular intervals. In this way, the inner boundaries of the cell walls appear to be more or less indented. These wavy walls of the lumen are characteristics by which you can recognize jute with a good degree of certainty (Fig. 83). However, in many cases you will need to observe carefully with high-power magnification in order to establish this characteristic unequivocally. The lumen of ramie displays walls which are similar in principle, but the ramie fibre is twice as wide as the jute fibre and not lignified. Jute is always somewhat lignified and therefore turns red with phloroglucinol and hydrochloric acid.

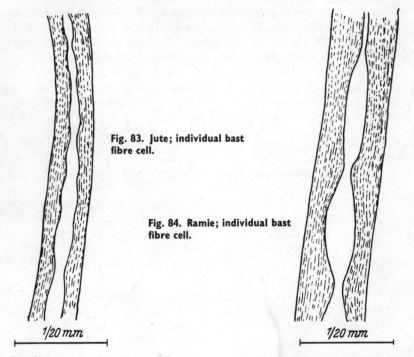

Fig. 83. Jute; individual bast fibre cell.

Fig. 84. Ramie; individual bast fibre cell.

1/20 mm

1/20 mm

Ramie

Ramie is understood to be the bast fibres from the plant, *Boehmeria*, which occurs in Asia. It is related to the stinging nettle, *Urtica*. Individual cells of the fibre are extremely long and very wide (according to Tober-Wolff, the diameter is 40–80μ). As with jute, the irregular, wavy course of the lumen is characteristic (Fig. 84). In spite of this, the ramie fibre can be distinguished from jute without trouble. First of all, the diameter of the individual fibre is almost twice the size of that of jute. Besides, jute is always lignified, whereas the walls of ramie fibres consist of nonlignified cellulose and accordingly turn a blue with zinc chloride and iodine, but never a red with phloroglucinol and hydrochloric acid.

In this connection, it should be pointed out that the stinging nettle can also be used as a plant for fibres. It contains bast fibres with properties which are not at all poor from the standpoint of the textile engineer. However, commercial utilization of the stinging nettle is confronted with several difficulties not to be underrated.

The stinging nettle is certainly considered a weed, but on closer examination it is not at all as widespread as might generally be assumed. The stinging nettle is found primarily in the vicinity of human dwellings, on compost heaps, refuse dumps, stables, etc., but hardly ever in large stands on open fields which are poor in nutrient substances. This indicates that the stinging nettle needs soil containing a large amount of nutrient substances, and, as a matter of fact, the stinging nettle does need a great deal of nitrogen. It would therefore not be worthwhile to cultivate it, since the fibre content is relatively low. Collecting wild stinging nettles is also not as easy as an inexperienced person might imagine. It not only takes a great deal of work to collect a worthwhile number of stalks from the stinging nettle, but it is almost impossible to gather a relatively uniform crop, for individual stands of stinging nettle differ in their degrees of maturity.

However, Tobler-Wolff emphasizes the fact that a cultivated fibre nettle has recently been obtained from the common stinging nettle, *Urtica dioica*. By suitable selection, the fibre content of the plant was significantly increased. Besides this, the cultivated fibre nettle is supposed to grow well on marshy soil.

Silk

Silk is a spun fibre which is excreted by the caterpillar of the moth, *Bombyx mori*, as a protective covering for the pupa. Two fibroin filaments emerge from the two spinning glands of this domesticated silkworm, and are immediately cemented together and surrounded by a common gelatinous covering, sericin. Raw silk is obtained by reeling off the cocoons from the pupae.

Raw silk is easy to recognize under the microscope by the two fibroin filaments which lie next to one another and are often enclosed by sericin, in the form of layers. Further treatment dissolves the sericin, whereupon the two fibroin filaments can usually be separated from one another. Thus,

163

worked-up silk appears under the microscope in the form of rather round, uniform threads in which no special structure can be seen (Fig. 85). In order to distinguish accurately between this worked-up silk and other fibres which are outwardly similar, you must again turn to microchemical reactions.

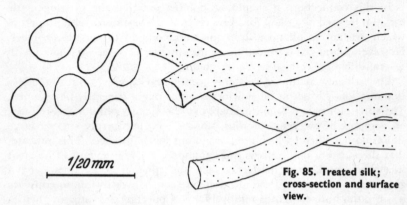

1/20 mm

Fig. 85. Treated silk; cross-section and surface view.

True silk dissolves in an alkaline solution of copper and glycerine. There is a considerable difference between this and, for example, cuprammonium rayon which often looks the same. Place the sample to be examined in a drop of an alkaline solution of copper and glycerine, cover with a cover-glass, and examine with medium-power magnification. If you are dealing with silk, you will soon be able to observe that the individual filaments begin to break apart, swell up in places, and finally dissolve from the ends. During this examination you must be very careful to prevent even the smallest drop of reagent from touching the microscope objective, since the strongly alkaline solution is extremely corrosive, and would ruin the expensive objective in a short time.

Quite often, tussah silk produced by the Chinese oak silkworm (*Antheraea pernyi*) is found in articles of commerce rather than true silk coming from the mulberry silkworm (*Bombyx mori*). Tussah silk is ribbon-like in structure and consequently appears to be elongated in cross-section. In contrast to true silk, tussah silk does not dissolve in a cold alkaline solution of copper and glycerine, but only in a hot one.

SEMI-SYNTHETIC FIBRES

In producing the more common semi-synthetic fibres, the chief structural material of the cell walls of plants, cellulose, is brought into the form of a viscous liquid. The cellulose solution is then drawn out by spinnerets into fibres which are then hardened in one way or another. There are a great many alternative methods of bringing cellulose into a form which can be spun. Essentially three processes prevail, the products of which are called viscose rayon, cuprammonium rayon, and acetate rayon according to the solvents employed in each case.

Viscose Rayon

Cellulose is converted into a viscous solution by treatment with alkalis and carbon disulphide. After a ripening process, the solution is forced through spinnerets into a spinning bath. The spinning baths may differ in composition, but always contain a great deal of sulphuric acid. The fibres formed in this way display a characteristic structure which makes them easy to recognize under the microscope.

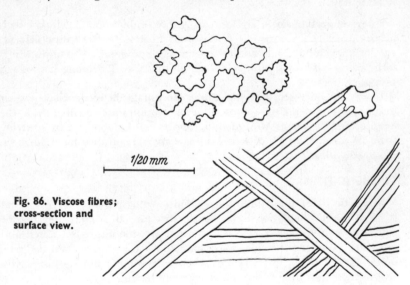

1/20 mm

Fig. 86. Viscose fibres; cross-section and surface view.

In a longitudinal view, the normal fibre of viscose rayon has slight flutelike striations which can hardly be confused with the lumens of natural vegetable fibres, since usually more than two striations can be seen in one view. You will recognize what causes striation from the cross-section. The fibre is lobate, and in addition, the individual lobes are often finely notched (Fig. 86).

It must be pointed out that certain fibres of viscose rayon produced by special processes look very much like fibres of cuprammonium rayon.

165

Cuprammonium Rayon

To produce fibres of cuprammonium rayon, the cellulose is dissolved in a solution of copper hydroxide and ammonia, and then is forced through spinnerets into water. The sulphuric acid bath, which follows, removes the copper from the fibres. Thus, the spinning baths remove most of the copper and ammonia again so that the name, cuprammonium fibre, is really misleading.

Fibres of cuprammonium rayon are usually smooth, appear to be structureless, and are round in cross-section. Externally they resemble silk, but they can be distinguished from it easily by their action in an alkaline solution of copper and glycerine. Fibres of cuprammonium rayon do not dissolve in alkaline copper and glycerine.

Acetate Rayon

Fibres of acetate rayon are formed by the combination of cellulose with acetic acid. This compound is dissolved in a suitable organic solvent, e.g., acetone and alcohol, and forced through spinnerets. The fibres which form are usually dried with warm air, so that a real spinning bath is not necessary.

Under the microscope acetate fibres can usually be recognized by their dumb-bell shape in cross-section. One or two lines are usually seen in the longitudinal direction. More definite results can be obtained by studying them in acetone, which dissolves the acetate fibres if they have not been modified with alkali.

SYNTHETIC FIBRES

Synthetic fibres present the microscopist with special problems. That is, they usually have no characteristic structure by which they can be easily recognized. Nylon, perlon and orlon are smooth, round fibres, and only the polyvinyl-chloride fibre has a structure which can be seen under the microscope. Therefore, when examining synthetic fibres, you will have to turn to microchemical reactions again.[18]

Nylon

Put a few threads of nylon into a solution of zinc chloride and iodine, place a cover-glass over them, and heat them over a small flame. When you do this, warm the microscope slide only enough so that it feels just tolerable when touched to the back of your hand. Examination with

---

[18] An excellent guide for these has been given by Heidenreich in *Mikrokosmos*, *42* (1952), 43.

the fibres are slightly indented at the edges. Now heat them more intensely. Under the microscope you will find that fibres heated intensely in zinc chloride and iodine will display coarsely indented edges and a structure on the inside that looks like a canal with coarse dotted lines. If it is heated until it boils, the nylon fibre will swell up a great deal (Fig. 87, 3–4).

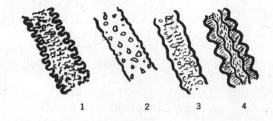

**Fig. 87. 1 and 2=Perlon;
3 and 4=Nylon.
See text for explanations.**

(Adapted from Heidenreich,
Mikrokosmos, *42*, 1952, 43.)

1   2   3   4

Perlon

Subject perlon fibres to the same test as nylon, i.e., place them in zinc chloride and iodine and warm them gently. The microscope shows that even after gentle heating perlon fibres appear to be markedly lobed at the edge, while nylon is only slightly indented after gentle heating. With more intense heating the lobes in perlon disappear, while only then do nylon fibres show distinct indentations. Perlon melts rapidly if heated until it boils (Fig. 87, 1–2).

Orlon

If orlon is placed in a solution of zinc chloride and iodine, the fibres swell up greatly and gradually go into solution. Because of this no individual threads can be recognized after a few minutes.

Polyvinyl-Chloride Fibres

PVC fibre consists of chlorinated polyvinyl chloride and is remarkably resistant to chemicals. In a longitudinal view of PVC fibre you will find a line running lengthwise, which, under certain circumstances, could be confused with the cellular cavity of a vegetable fibre. Of course, the experienced microscopist would recognize the fibre immediately by its uniform shape, but in any case you can still employ a chemical test:

All vegetable fibres swell up in sodium hydroxide while PVC fibres are not attacked. Thus, if the material to be examined is placed in a 10% solution of sodium hydroxide and no signs of swelling are present after 10 to 15 minutes of observation, a PVC fibre might be present. If there is swelling, it is probably a vegetable fibre which must now be identified more precisely.

The following table may serve to facilitate the identification of the more common synthetic fibres for the inexperienced microscopist:

The fibre is dyed violet with zinc chloride and iodine...............see 1
The fibre is dyed yellow with zinc chloride and iodine............see 2
1—Cross-section is lobed (longitudinal striation):   viscose rayon
   —Cross-section has smooth outlines: cuprammonium rayon
2—Fibre dissolves in acetone: acetate rayon
   —Fibre dissolves after a few minutes in a solution of
     cold zinc chloride and iodine: orlon
   —Edge of the fibre is markedly lobate after gentle
     heating in zinc chloride and iodine: perlon
   —Slight indentations at the edge of the fibre after
     gentle warming in zinc chloride and iodine: nylon

You have now become acquainted with the most important textile fibres and can now proceed to the real problem: examination of mixed fabrics as usually found in textiles. Perhaps many of you will have a few surprises if you now examine your clothing thoroughly.

Of course, it is when examining mixed fabrics that you must use the microchemical reactions described above. When doing this, note that all reagents must have enough time to act on the fibres. Therefore, before evaluating the result of a reaction, always wait for a few minutes. Besides, you should not forget that most fibres are artificially dyed, a fact that often leads the beginner to make errors. Dyes and delustrants are added to many synthetic fibres even before they are drawn out into individual threads. In this case, these substances are found within the fibre itself. Finally, it must be mentioned that many synthetic fibres are proteinized. An effort is made to make the fibres more like natural wool by depositing nitrogen-containing compounds in them. Such proteinized fibres are usually treated with different dyes from those used on fibres which have not received preliminary treatment. For this reason, no attempt has been made above to deal with dyeing reactions currently used.

Examination of textiles offers the microscopist a broad field which is almost inexhaustible. As in all microscope work, patience and experience also lead most surely to success in their field.

IDENTIFYING TEXTILE FIBRES

The instructions given above are sufficient for most of the simpler examinations of fibres. For the reader who is especially interested in this field there are several books available, as well as charts.[19]

PREPARATION OF THE REAGENTS NEEDED FOR THE EXAMINATION OF TEXTILES

1. PHLOROGLUCINOL—HYDROCHLORIC ACID

Dissolve 1 gm. phloroglucinol in 50 cc. absolute alcohol. Immediately before use, add one part by volume of concentrated hydrochloric acid to two parts by volume of this solution. Lignified fibres are stained red in phloroglucinol-hydrochloric acid.

2. COPPER HYDROXIDE—AMMONIA (Cuprammonium or Schweitzer's reagent)

Pour concentrated ammonia over some cupric oxide so that a solution which is deep blue is formed. The solution cannot be kept and must therefore be freshly prepared before use. In many cases, you can do without this reagent. Cuprammonium dissolves cellulose, while lignified and corked cell walls are not dissolved. In cuprammonium, many fibres display characteristic swelling phenomena which can be used for identification.

3. ZINC CHLORIDE—IODINE

A solution of zinc chloride and iodine stains cellulose violet to blue and is therefore important for distinguishing between lignified and non-lignified cell walls. The solution consists of:

Zinc chloride ....50 parts by weight
Potassium iodide......16 parts by weight
Iodine .... 3 parts by weight
Distilled water.........20 parts by weight

4. ALKALINE COPPER—GLYCERINE

Prepare the following copper sulphate solution:
Copper sulphate...... 10 parts by weight
Water ....100 parts by weight
Glycerine.............. 5 parts by weight

Add concentrated sodium hydroxide to this solution. A thick precipitate is formed which dissolves when more sodium hydroxide is added. In general, add enough sodium hydroxide to dissolve the precipitate which was first formed completely.

---

[19] A chart can be found in a booklet published by "Deutsche Rhodiaceta A.G.," Freiburg im Breisgau: M.-L. Bumiller: "Schnellmethoden zur Identifizierung von Textilfasern." This work of Bumiller first appeared in "Reyon, Zellwolle und andere Chemiefasern," 9 (1956), 612–617. Further reference works are: H. R. Mauersberger, *Mathews' Textile Fibers*, 5th edition, John Wiley, New York, 1947, R. W. Moncrieff, *Man-Made Fibers*, John Wiley, New York, 1957, L. A. Olney, *Textile Chemistry and Dyeing, Part I, 10th edition. Chemical Technology of the Fiber*, Lowell Textile Association, Lowell, Massachusetts, 1947, J. H. Shinkle, *Textile Testing*, 2nd edition. Chemical Publishing Company, Brooklyn, 1949.

10. Testing Paper

Microscopic examination of paper is important in technology, trade, and industry. The quality of a paper and its suitability for certain purposes depend largely upon its composition.

Paper can be manufactured from different kinds of raw materials. Plant fibres are generally used and the plants from which they come can be identified only by microscopic observation. For a start, fibres can be divided very roughly into 3 groups:

1. Fibres from rags
2. Groundwood (or mechanical) pulp, and
3. Chemical wood pulp

BREAKING UP THE PAPER AND MAKING PREPARATIONS

Take bits from different sections of the paper you are going to examine and soften them in water. Shred the well-soaked bits of paper and boil them in 1% sodium hydroxide (caustic soda). Some care should be taken in doing this, since boiling alkali spatters easily. It is best to boil the sample in a small heat-resistant glass beaker. After it has cooled, shake the sample well with 1% sodium hydroxide or water in a test tube. Shaking produces a suspension of fine filaments which will gradually settle at the bottom of the tube after standing. If you have a centrifuge at your disposal, you can wash the suspension of fibres with water to remove the sodium hydroxide. In case you don't have a centrifuge, you can wash a small quantity with water on a microscope slide. Larger pieces, which have not been completely reduced to fibres, can be teased out fine on the slide with the help of two needles.

Two reagents greatly facilitate the examination of paper: a solution of zinc chloride-iodine and phloroglucinol-hydrochloric acid (see p. 169).

If you examine the sample, which has been reduced to fibres and washed, in a solution of zinc chloride-iodine:

fibres coming from rags are stained red
groundwood fibres are stained yellow
and chemical wood pulp fibres are stained blue

It must be pointed out that reactions with zinc chloride-iodine are often not completely specific as to shade. Do not fail to examine the structures carefully in all cases. In general, phloroglucinol-hydrochloric acid is used to distinguish between fibres of groundwood and chemical wood pulp.

Neither zinc chloride-iodine nor phloroglucinol-hydrochloric acid are suitable for making permanent preparations, but you can make permanent preparations successfully with the somewhat complicated fuchsine-aniline blue stain described on p. 31—mount with a synthetic mounting medium.

RAG FIBRES

Rag papers are considered to be especially good. However, papers which have been manufactured from rags alone have become relatively rare today. You already know the fibres used—primarily cotton, hemp, flax, and occasionally even wool—from the previous chapter, Textile Fibres. But you must bear in mind that the fibres have been strongly attacked in the manufacture of paper. In most cases, you will still be able to recognize the characteristic features of the individual fibres, but occasionally the fibres have been so thoroughly shredded, crushed, and split up into individual filaments (fibrilized), that it is possible to classify them with certainty only if you have a great deal of experience.

GROUNDWOOD PULP

Lignified fibres in paper are usually from wood pulp that has been mechanically ground. Groundwood pulp is stained a bright red by phloroglucinol-hydrochloric acid. The particles of groundwood pulp usually still show clearly the structures of wood which you already know. In soft wood groundwood pulp, you will recognize the large pits of the tracheids without difficulty. It stands to reason that usually only fragments of the original tissue occur in particles of groundwood pulp. Despite your knowledge of the structure of native woods, therefore, it is difficult for you to identify with certainty the plant from which the groundwood pulp comes. However, in practice it is usually enough to know that groundwood pulp is actually present and whether it comes from soft or hard wood. As you know, you can recognize hard wood by the presence of tracheae, i.e., vessels with end walls which are discontinuous or open like a ladder (see Chapter 4 on Woods).

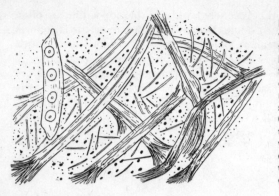

Fig. 88. Cigarette paper which has been reduced to fibres. It has been finely beaten and a great deal of filter added. The paper consists chiefly of pure, nonlignified plant fibres, such as flax and hemp. Other constituents, such as the tracheids from soft wood (which have been drawn in), are so rare that they can almost be considered mere impurities.

CHEMICAL WOOD PULP FIBRES

To produce chemical wood pulp (also falsely called cellulose), parts of plants are chemically freed of lignin. Therefore, chemical wood pulp can be distinguished from groundwood without difficulty by means of the phloroglucinol-hydrochloric acid reaction. Since lignin has been removed from chemical wood pulp, phloroglucinol-hydrochloric acid does not stain it at all or—if the lignin has not been completely removed—only slightly.

In spite of the chemical treatment, you can still recognize the structure of individual plant cells in chemical wood pulp clearly. The tissue formation has usually come apart, so that individual fibres prevail.

Just as in groundwood, soft woods are usually preferred to hard woods in the production of chemical wood pulp. In this case too, soft woods can be distinguished from hard woods by the structure of their vessels. The most generally used soft woods are the conifers, and among the hard woods especially poplar, beech, and birch.

Paper pulp is very often obtained from straw. The epidermal cells, the walls of which are more or less wavy, are a characteristic guide to recognizing straw pulp (Fig. 89). Elongated, sclerenchymal fibres, which are often very thick, make up the bulk of straw pulp. Besides these, there are (more rarely) thin-walled parenchymal cells (also called sack cells by specialists) and vessels.

Esparto pulp is frequently used. It comes from a type of grass, *Stipa tenacissima*, native to Spain and North Africa and is similar to straw pulp. However, the parenchymal cells which occur in straw pulp are not usually present in esparto pulp. In addition, small, claw-shaped hairs are always found in esparto papers.

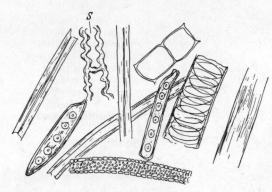

Fig. 89. Corrugated board, consisting of straw pulp and soft wood pulp, reduced to fibres. S= epidermal cells from straw, an important characteristic for straw pulp.

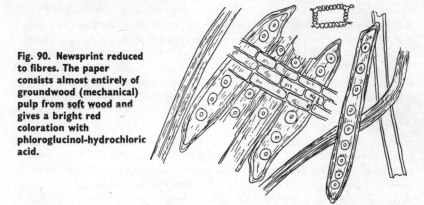

Fig. 90. Newsprint reduced to fibres. The paper consists almost entirely of groundwood (mechanical) pulp from soft wood and gives a bright red coloration with phloroglucinol-hydrochloric acid.

EVALUATION OF PAPER QUALITY

The microscope not only gives information on the composition of a paper from different kinds of fibres, but it also shows how long the fibres are, how fine they are, and what sort of sizing and filling materials were added in the manufacture.

For example, fine writing papers and banknote paper have longer fibres than newsprint or filter papers. In addition, each type of paper has various grades of quality, and you can differentiate between high and low quality kraft papers, for example, under the microscope by observing the texture of the fibres, the tighter textures indicating greater strength.[20]

---

[20] For further information on paper, consult: J. P. Casey, *Pulp and Paper*, 2nd edition, volume 3: *Paper Testing and Converting*, New York and London, Interscience Publishers, Inc., 1961, E. M. Chamot and C. W. Mason, *Handbook of Chemical Microscopy*, 3rd edition, New York and London, John Wiley, 1958, J. N. Stephenson, ed., *Manufacture and Testing of Paper and Board*, volume 3, 1st edition, New York and London, McGraw-Hill, 1953.

11. Bacteria and Fungi

The importance of bacteria and fungi for higher animals and plants can scarcely be overestimated. The transformation of substances in the soil, so important for plant life, is caused largely by these micro-organisms; the self-purification of water, also of the greatest consequence for human beings, is largely the work of bacteria; and the removal of organic waste products is carried out by bacteria everywhere in the world. All of the functions which micro-organisms fulfil in the balance of nature would take pages to enumerate, yet many people know little more about bacteria than that they can produce diseases.

To a continually increasing extent, man consciously utilizes the diverse abilities of micro-organisms for his purposes. You have only to think of the following activities, which are completely dependent upon micro-organisms: brewing industry; cheese production; the production of citric acid by the mould, *Aspergillus niger*; and the formation of antibiotic substances, such as penicillin, by moulds and other microbes.

Many microscopists do not trust themselves to work with bacteria, because they assume that excellent laboratory facilities, such as specialists have at their disposal, are necessary. It is true that extensive activities with large amounts of material to be examined can only be performed in well-organized laboratories. However, within narrower limits and with unpretentious goals, it is also possible to obtain practically useful results with primitive means.

If you want to become acquainted with a species of bacteria, mould, or yeast more closely, it is necessary to culture the organism under consideration and to establish pure cultures of it. Then, on the basis of the pure culture, it is possible to observe its properties. In this way, it can be important to establish which nutrients an organism needs for growth, whether it forms industrially useful metabolic products, whether the fermentation it causes leads to a product of higher or lower quality, and whether the yield could be commercially profitable.

174

Unfortunately, it is difficult to identify the species of micro-organisms, especially bacteria. But to be able to work with a micro-organism, it is not at all necessary to know what it actually is. If an organism you have cultured should have properties which seem worth evaluating, you can have it identified by a specialist since it is present in a pure culture.

Unfortunately, it is not within the scope of this book to describe in more detail the possibilities for using micro-organisms in industry. One example might suffice:

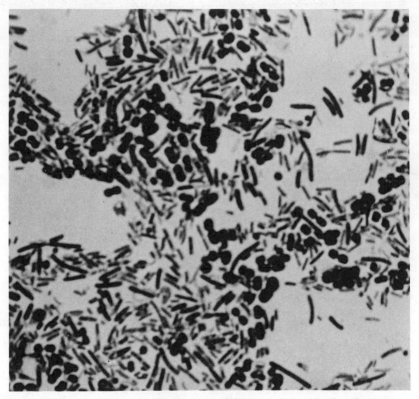

Illus. 13. Bacteria from the scum of a hay infusion (magnification about 1,000×; photo by M. P. Kage).

Like all living things, micro-organisms also produce enzymes, i.e., substances which can split certain chemical compounds even when highly diluted. Thus, cellulases split cellulose into sugars, lipases split fat into fatty acids and glycerine, and proteases split protein into amino acids.

Now, enzymes formed by micro-organisms can be obtained very easily. For this reason, bacteria and fungi are often used for the production of enzymes in industry and medicine. We have preparations today which enable man to utilize to a large degree even the cellulose walls of plant cells for his food. These preparations contain the enzyme cellulase which converts cellulose into sugars. If you take an appropriate cellulase preparation at mealtimes, a large part of the cell walls from plant foods will be converted into sugar in your intestine and thus made available to your body. It is just this cellulase which industry obtains largely from micro-organisms.

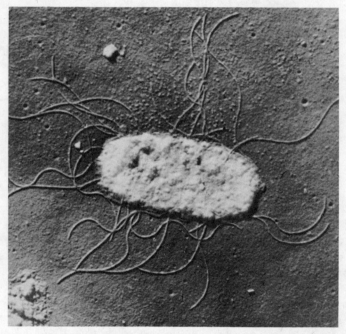

Illus. 14. Proteus bacillus showing its many flagella (magnification about 13,570×). (Photo courtesy Dr. R. Wyckoff, National Institutes of Health.)

Many possibilities for industrial utilization of micro-organisms are still unexploited. Even if specialists work intensively in this field, a wide area still remains for the outsider to consider. A prerequisite for each successful study with micro-organisms is a knowledge of the techniques of examining them. Let us now deal with this.

FORMS OF BACTERIA

Let us first become acquainted with the different forms of bacteria. Since bacteria can be found practically everywhere, it is not difficult to procure material. To find large quantities of bacteria, you need only to look at some decaying material under the microscope. You will find an especially great number of various forms if you place about 2 to 3 cm. of soil in a container, cover it with a layer of water and let a few pieces of meat decay there. Countless bacteria can also be seen after several days in infusions of hay. In such infusions, the bacteria are primarily at the surface where, in time, a film of "mould" is formed which consists entirely of bacteria.

Bacteria are tiny, unicellular organisms. The smallest are no longer than 1μ and scarcely $\frac{1}{4}\mu$ wide. Bacteria were formerly described, among other things, as unicellular organisms without a nucleus and without photosynthetic pigments. But more recent studies show that there are structures in the cell body of bacteria corresponding to the nucleus of higher organisms; also, it has been known for a long time that a few bacteria have a photosynthetic pigment. The more that is known about bacteria, the more difficult it becomes to differentiate between them and other groups of organisms. In nature, there are simply no rigidly delimited, isolated forms; transitional forms can always be found at some point.

For a long time it was thought that bacteria were the original forms from which other organisms developed. Undoubtedly, bacteria have the simplest structure of the organisms we know. (The still more primitive viruses cannot be counted among living things with complete certainty.) However, this simple structure could also be a regression or degeneration which occurred in the course of evolution. If you consider the varied physiological feats which these primitive organisms can perform, you can see that it is necessary to look for the origin of life in still more simply organized forms.

Most bacteria are heterotrophic—that is, they need organic substances as nutrients and cannot synthesize organic compounds from inorganic ones as autotrophic (self-nourishing) organisms do. Just from this fact you can draw a conclusion of practical importance: organic substances must be present wherever bacteria thrive. Thus, for example, if you find many bacteria in a body of water, you can safely say that it is heavily contaminated with organic substances. (A few autotrophic thread-forming bacteria and autotrophic sulphur bacteria are exceptions, but these can easily be recognized as such.)

Under high-power magnification you will see a wild swarm of the most diverse kinds of bacteria in a drop of stagnant water. You will find motile

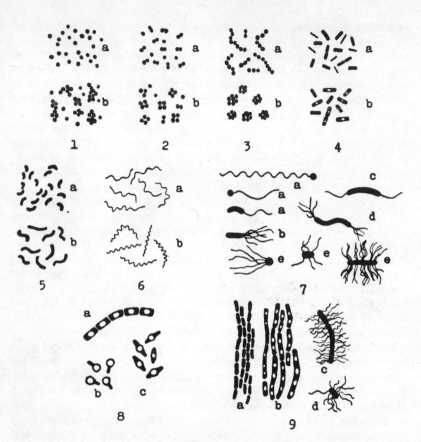

Fig. 91. Various forms of bacteria. 1a=micrococci; 1b=micrococci clusters (Staphylococci); 2a=combination of two micrococci (diplococci); 2b= combination of four micrococci (tetracocci); 3a=Streptococci; 3b=Sarcinae (cocci packets); 4a=rods without spores (Bacteria); 4b=rods with spores (Bacillae); 5a=vibriones; 5b=spirillae; 6a=spirochetes (tartar from teeth); 6b=spirochetes (causative organism of syphilis); 7a=bacterial flagellae, unipolar (monotrichic); 7b=bacterial flagellae, unipolar (lophotrichic); 7c= bacterial flagellae, dipolar (monotrichic); 7d=bacterial flagellae, bipolar (lophotrichic); 7e=bacterial flagellae, multipolar (peritrichic); 8a=bacterial spores (located in the middle); 8b=bacterial spores, drumstick form (located at one end); 8c=bacterial spores, watch-hand form (located in the middle); 9a= Hay Bacillus, chain structure (scum); 9b=Hay Bacillus, chains of cells with spores; 9c=Hay Bacillus, cell nuclei (showing flagellae); 9d=Hay Bacillus, swarm cells (showing flagellae).

(Adapted from Erdmann, *Mikrokosmos, 41*, 1952, 91.)

or nonmotile rods (bacilli) separately or connected in whole chains, forms which look like twisted threads and wind among the crowd of other bacteria with astonishing speed; nonmotile spheres (cocci) are found separately or are assembled like chains or packets. Many bacilli probably contain bodies on the inside which shine brightly and can be located in the middle or can swell up the end like a drum stick (Fig. 91).

So that you can survey this confusing abundance of forms, you must first create order. In doing this, we will first use the classification system that botanists use, as it is simpler for beginners, based as it is primarily on shapes. Bacteriologists usually use the nomenclature of Bergey, which is preferable for them because it subdivides large groups of bacteria, e.g., the genera *Bacillus* and *Bacterium*, and takes into account their physical and chemical properties. However, the broad outlines of the botanical system are retained here. (In cases where the botanical nomenclature differs from Bergey's, the latter is given in parentheses.)

Order I. Eubacteriales

(NOTE: *Genus is in italics capitalized, species italics not capitalized.*)

The Eubacteriales are unicellular, unbranched forms. By far the majority of all bacteria belong to this order.

Eubacteriales are subdivided into 3 families: Coccaceae, Bacteriaceae, and Spirillaceae. (In Bergey, 3 suborders: Eubacteriineae, Caulobacteriineae, Rhodobacteriineae.)

COCCACEAE FAMILY. The Coccaceae (cocci) are spherical in shape, usually very small, nonmotile bacteria. They can be found singly; united in chains, e.g., as the dreaded *Streptococci*, the cause of suppuration; and occasionally combined in pairs (called diplococci), e.g., Gonococci (*Neisseria gonorrhoeae*), the causative organisms of gonorrhea which are shaped like coffee beans. They can be deposited in grape-like clusters like *Staphylococci*, the causative organism of most harmless suppurations, and can be arranged like cubical packets (*Sarcinae*).

BACTERIACEAE FAMILY. The Bacteriaceae ("bacteria" in the narrower sense) are rod-shaped, motile or nonmotile cells.

The genus *Bacterium* is incapable of spore formation. Among innumerable well-known bacteria, the *Rhizobium radicicola* which lives in the root tubercles of leguminous plants belongs here. A symbiosis has occurred in this plant. This bacteria is capable of binding nitrogen from the atmosphere and thus making it available to the higher plant. Because of this, leguminous plants can be cultivated on soils which are very poor in nitrogen if *Rhizobium radicicola* is present. Moreover, in some cases, soils can also be inoculated with this bacteria.

Bacillus Genus. Like *Bacteria*, the *Bacilli* are rod-shaped, motile or nonmotile cells. But they can form spores, an ability which the *Bacteria* do not possess. The spores of *Bacilli* are permanent forms which make it possible for the organisms to withstand unsuitable environmental conditions and to overcome them. For example, if they dry out slowly or there is a deficiency of nutrients, a round or oval body surrounded by a resistant membrane, the spore, forms in the inside of the cell. If the *Bacillus* cell disintegrates, the spore is set free. It is interesting and of practical importance to know that spores are capable of withstanding extreme environmental conditions. Thus, at boiling heat, vegetative cells are rapidly destroyed. But spores, to a large extent, can easily withstand even hours of boiling. They are not damaged at all by drying out and intense cold, and they are even remarkably resistant to the action of chemicals. Thus, it can be explained that the hay bacillus, for example, which every microscopist knows from infusions, is found almost everywhere. If the puddles in which hay bacilli have lived and multiplied dry up, the spores can be blown away by the wind. If a spore falls in a suitable medium, e.g., in a small pond containing plant residues, it germinates to form a new hay bacillus which then multiplies extremely quickly under suitable conditions.

Naturally you cannot decide easily whether a form which has been found belongs to the genus *Bacterium* or to the genus *Bacillus*. Of course, it could happen that *Bacilli* have not yet formed any spores at all. In such cases, you try to force the cells to form spores. Place a drop of the culture broth on a cover-glass, turn this over rapidly so that the drop hangs from the bottom, and place it over the cavity in a hollow-ground microscope slide. Place a drop of mineral oil at the four corners of the cover-glass. It is sucked under the cover-glass by capillary action and seals the space formed between cover-glass and slide tightly. Bacteria found in the hanging drop will multiply still further at the beginning, but soon the living conditions become unsuitable for them in the narrow space. If you are dealing with members of the genus *Bacillus*, they will form spores which can be found easily with the microscope, while no spore formation occurs in the genus *Bacterium* (Fig. 92).

Butyric acid bacilli (genus *Butyribacterium*) are especially suitable for the study of spores in bacilli. There is a well-known disease in potatoes called damp rot. The causative organism of damp rot is the butyric acid bacillus, a relatively large, rod-shaped bacteria which is anaerobic, i.e., can only live if atmospheric oxygen is completely excluded. You can produce damp rot artificially: prick an unmashed potato deeply in several places and then place it in a container with water. The water should

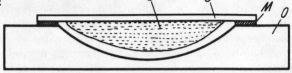

Fig. 92. Culture of micro-organisms in a hanging drop (schematic cross-section through a hollow-ground microscope slide). C=cover-glass; O=slide with depression; M=mineral oil; D=drop with nutrient material.

stand high above the potato. Depending upon the temperature, the contents of the potato will be changed into a pulpy, stinking mass within a few days or 1 to 2 weeks. The potato then rises to the surface because of gas formation. If you now remove a small sample of the rotted pulp and dilute it with water on a microscope slide, you will be able to see a large number of rods from the butyric acid bacilli. Many of these bacilli have on the inside in the middle a large, brightly shining spore.

SPIRILLACEAE FAMILY. Spirillaceae or spirilla are, as their name indicates, coiled. Of course, there are also forms here with turns which do not form complete coils: vibriones, to which, for example, the causative organism of cholera (*Vibrio comma*) belongs. You can find spirilla especially in heavily contaminated water. In particular, water which contains manure and also manure itself almost always contain innumerable spirilla. Rotting blood is also a good culture medium for many species of spirilla. You will almost never look for spirilla in vain in it, but you will need a relatively experienced eye to find the coils in living, motile spirilla. Because they usually shoot so quickly through the field of vision, you will have trouble following them with your eye.

Order II. Actinomycetales

The Actinomycetales (Mycobacteriales) are usually nonmotile bacilli. However, in contrast to the Eubacteriales, they can form branches under certain conditions. In this order belong several dangerous pathogenic agents, e.g., *Mycobacterium tuberculosis*, the causative organism of tuberculosis, and *Corynebacterium diphtheriae*, the causative organism of diphtheria. The ray fungi, the *Actinomyces* which have given the name to the entire order, are important. The ray fungi can grow into organisms several centimetres in size, each of which consist of a single, delicate, thread-shaped cell. However, under certain circumstances they can also form bacteria-like rods. A ray fungus, *Actinomyces bovis*, is the causative organism of the dreaded ray fungus disease, actinomycosis (lumpy jaw), in man

181

and animals. The ray fungi have a prominent place among micro-organisms in the soil. Many transformations in the soil, important for agriculture and forestry, are brought about chiefly by ray fungi. Thus, the ray fungi also have a prominent role in the formation of humus. In recent years the ray fungi have also moved into the range of medicine, that is, many of them form antibiotic substances of which Streptomycin (obtained from the ray fungus *Streptomyces griseus*) is especially well known. *Streptomyces* normally occurs in the soil.

Order III. Chlamydobacteriales

Beginners often confuse the Chlamydobacteriales (Trichobacteriales) or thread-forming bacteria under the microscope with fungi. The cells of these bacteria form long threads which are often slimy, but these threads are much thinner than fungal hyphae. It is interesting that among the thread-forming bacteria there are autotrophic forms, i.e., can form organic substances themselves and are not dependent upon the addition of organic substances from the outside. The autotrophy of these organisms does not depend upon the utilization of energy from sunlight with the aid of a photosynthetic pigment as in green plants; instead, autotrophic thread-forming bacteria obtain the energy which they need from chemical reactions. Thus, this is a rare case of chemosynthesis in contrast to the photosynthesis of chlorophyll-containing plants. Moreover, many investigators hypothesize that the first living things on earth met their energy requirements by such chemosynthesis and that photosynthesis, which is connected with digestive pigments, developed only at a later time.

CHLAMYDOBACTERIACEAE FAMILY. The Chlamydobacteriaceae consist of threads attached to one another. Each individual thread is surrounded by a sheath. You cannot see this sheath in ordinary preparations. However, if you add a drop of India ink to the preparation, then the sheaths will appear bright on a dark background at suitable spots (where the suspension of India ink is not too thick and not too thin).

The highly interesting, largely autotrophic iron bacteria, e.g., the common species *Leptothrix*, belong to the Chlamydobacteriaceae. The iron bacteria oxidize ferrous carbonate in waters which contain iron and thus obtain energy. The oxidized iron is deposited in the sheaths in the form of ferric hydroxide. A part of the energy obtained in this way can be used for synthesizing organic substances from inorganic compounds (chemosynthesis). You could almost say that iron bacteria breathe iron salts! This is an interesting process which has a practical side in addition.

If iron bacteria grow at the same place over long periods of time, whole layers of iron ore, bog iron ore, are formed from iron stored in the sheaths. In many places so much bog iron ore has formed during the course of time that it is actually profitable to mine it.

Iron bacteria can often be recognized by the fact that iron stored in the sheaths is visible even with the naked eye as a rust-red precipitate. BEGGIATOACEAE FAMILY. (Recently placed among the blue algae—Cyanophyceae.) The Beggiatoaceae or sulphur bacteria also consist of long threads which can even creep on substrata, but in contrast to the Chlamydobacteriaceae have no sheaths. Sulphur bacteria also are autotrophic through chemosynthesis. At the bottom of many bodies of water there is plenty of hydrogen sulphide from the decomposition of protein found in the remains of plants and animals and from other sources. Sulphur bacteria are now in the position to oxidize this hydrogen sulphide to sulphur and even to sulphuric acid and to obtain energy from this process. Thus, if iron bacteria breathe iron salts, the sulphur bacteria use hydrogen sulphide as respiratory material.

Order IV. Myxobacteriales

The Myxobacteria or slime bacteria can be found quite frequently in animal excrement. They live in colonies consisting of swarms of rod-shaped cells. These swarms can creep and secrete slime in the process. Occasionally all of the rods creep together to one place and thus form an aggregation which is called the fruiting body (but these structures have nothing to do with the fruiting bodies of fungi). New swarms of bacteria are freed from the fruiting bodies.

Order V. Spirochaetales

Probably the spirochetes are not at all related to bacteria. However, since the methods for examining bacteria and spirochetes are largely the same, and since bacteria and spirochetes often occur together, they are mentioned here. (Spirochetes as a rule are not readily stained by ordinary stains like methylene blue. Special stains such as Giemsa's, which stain protozoa, also stain the spirochetes.) Spirochetes are delicate, sinuous organisms often confused with spirilla by beginners, but they are much more coiled than the spirilla. Among other places, spirochetes can be found in tartar on the teeth. *Treponema* (*Spirochaete*) *pallidum* is the causative organism for syphilis.

As far as is known today, the reproduction of bacteria is asexual, always by binary fission of the cells; this occurs vertically at the longitudinal axis in rod-shaped species. Under hospitable conditions many species of bacteria can divide once in 20–30 minutes. If you calculate from this how many bacteria could be formed in 12 hours under optimum conditions from one initial cell, multiplying every half-hour, you will obtain 11,577,216 bacteria. Of course, it is not really as bad as all that, for when multiplying this quickly, living conditions for the organisms deteriorate almost to the same extent as propagation progresses, so that cell divisions are inhibited. However, propagation does occur extremely rapidly. You can make use of this fact in setting up cultures.

STAINING METHODS

You must fix and stain the bacteria to examine them thoroughly. There is no need to be so careful as with cells and tissues of higher organisms. You can simply allow the bacteria to dry out—a gross error in most cases with other objects. However, the inside of the bacterial cell lies largely beneath the resolving power of your microscope, so you do not have to worry about destroying the internal structures: however you do it, you can only see the contours.

Place a small drop of material containing bacteria on a completely dry cover-glass cleaned with alcohol and spread the drop in as uniform a layer as possible. Allow the smear to dry in the air but protect it from dust. Then, to fix the bacteria, pass the cover-glass with the dry smear 3 times in succession very quickly through a flame at brief intervals with the smear side up. Next, drop the stain solution on the smear, and use enough so that the cover-glass is covered with stain.

Preferably use fuchsine and methylene blue as stains. Fuchsine stains rod-shaped bacteria especially well, methylene blue, the cocci.

PREPARATION OF CARBOL FUCHSINE SOLUTION: Dissolve enough basic fuchsine in 70% alcohol so that a sediment is formed which does not dissolve, even with persistent shaking. This saturated solution, the stock solution, can be kept for a long time. The staining solution is prepared from it by diluting one part by volume of the stock solution with 10 parts by volume of water and adding 5% phenol to it. This carbol fuchsine can also be bought ready-for-use, which is naturally more convenient, but also more expensive than if you prepare it yourself. (Another method is to dissolve 0.3 gm. basic fuchsine in 10 cc. 95% ethyl alcohol, mix with 100 cc. of 5% aqueous phenol.)

PREPARATION OF METHYLENE BLUE SOLUTION: A saturated alcoholic stock solution is first prepared, just as with the fuchsine solution. The staining solution is obtained by diluting the stock solution with water in a 1:5 ratio. You can buy ready-to-use Löffler's methylene blue solution on the market which, in addition, contains a trace of potassium hydroxide and can be highly recommended.

You will want to stain the first preparation with fuchsine, since fuchsine stains most bacteria more intensely than methylene blue. Allow the stain to act on the smear for about 5 minutes, then pour it off and rinse the cover-glass under tap water. After immersing it for a short time in distilled water, put the cover-glass away to dry. In doing so, it is advisable to stand it on edge on a base of blotting paper. When the smear has become quite dry, place the cover-glass with the smear side down in a drop of Canada balsam or a synthetic mounting medium on a microscope slide. The permanent preparation is then ready.

In successful preparations the bacteria appear deep, dark red on a bright (but in any case, light) reddish background. But you might also find that the entire preparation is interspersed with irregular, ugly red spots which are quite definitely not bacteria. This occurs if the cover-glass has not been well cleaned or if the medium in which the bacteria were found contained fatty substances. In the latter case, you can find a way out by immersing the cover-glass several times in ether after the smear has dried but before you fix it; then allow it to dry again.

A commonly used, valuable staining method is Gram's stain. The method depends upon the fact that many species of bacteria retain the stain when they are differentiated after staining in crystal violet (see below) and others give it off again. Thus, according to the result of staining, you can distinguish between Gram-positive and Gram-negative bacteria; determining whether a species of bacteria which is being studied is Gram-positive or Gram-negative can be a valuable clue for identifying the species. However, it must be emphasized that staining does not always give entirely regular results. Even Gram-positive bacteria can sometimes react as Gram-negative ones under certain conditions, and the stain can produce quite variable results with Gram-variable bacteria.

For Gram staining you will need a carbol crystal violet solution, a carbol fuchsine solution, and a solution of iodine and potassium iodine (Lugol's solution, see page 8).

PREPARATION OF THE CARBOL CRYSTAL VIOLET SOLUTION: Dilute one part by volume of a saturated crystal violet solution in 70% alcohol with 10 parts by volume of distilled water and, in addition, add 5% phenol to the diluted solution. For preparation of the carbol fuchsine solution, see the previous page.

To fix, pass an air-dried smear of material containing bacteria on a cover-glass 3 times through a flame, as described above. Next stain for 3 minutes with carbol crystal violet solution. In some cases, it is advisable to warm the smear quite gently during staining. Then pour off (do not rinse off) the stain solution and replace it with Lugol's solution. Allow it to act for about 2 minutes. Rinse off the Lugol's solution with water and counter-stain for about half a minute with dilute carbol fuchsine solution (1 part by volume carbol fuchsine solution, 10 parts by volume water). After rinsing the fuchsine solution off under tap water, let the smear dry in the air or high over a flame. Mount in a synthetic mounting medium.

Microscopic examination of a smear stained according to Gram's method will show you the Gram-positive bacteria—those which have not given off the crystal violet during differentiation in alcohol—in deep blue, while the Gram-negative bacteria are stained red. They have given off the crystal violet again and thus display the red tinge of the carbol fuchsine stain.

To detect spores in a stained preparation, you must use a special method since the spores of *Bacilli* cannot be shown with conventional staining techniques. That is, the membrane of spores is so impermeable that the stains cannot penetrate into the spores at all. Therefore, before staining you must use reagents which attack the spore membranes or at least make them less impermeable. This is how to stain spores:[21]

Fix the air-dried smear well (pass it through a flame several times) and put a 5% aqueous solution of chromic acid on it for 2 to 10 minutes. After rinsing it off with water, cover the smear with plenty of carbol fuchsine and heat it over the flame. When fumes from the stain begin to rise, remove the cover-glass from the immediate vicinity of the flame and hold it for a minute so that the stain solution remains quite hot, but does not come to a boil. Then rinse it off with water and immerse the cover-glass for a few seconds in 5% sulphuric acid. The stain is removed from the bacteria again by treatment in sulphuric acid. However, since the spores do not give the stain off again as rapidly as the rest of the bacterial body, a time is reached at which only the spores are still stained. It is just at this point that differentiation must be discontinued by rinsing the sulphuric acid off with water. Naturally it takes some experience to estimate correctly the length of time which the smear must remain in sulphuric acid. It is recommended that staining be checked under the microscope after rinsing off the sulphuric acid. Finally, stain again with aqueous methylene blue solution. This will stain the previously destained bacterial bodies blue. Thus, in successful preparations the spores must be

---

[21] The method used by Möller for spore staining is described.

stained red, the other constituents of the bacteria, a blue. Of course, the blue counter-staining will not give the clarity desired in all cases since, in some cases, a large part of the bacterial cytoplasm has been used for spore formation.

In your observations of living bacteria you have already noticed that many bacteria are motile, but others are nonmotile. Motile bacteria are equipped with fine, filamentous processes, the whiplike flagellae, with the aid of which they can direct their movement. Often it is important to determine whether a bacterium is motile or nonmotile. This problem can be solved most simply by examining living preparations under the microscope. However, in examining them you must consider that bacteria can also display movements which are not active, spontaneous movements. Here error is caused by Brownian (molecular) movement in particular. Very minute bodies, such as bacteria, which can just barely be seen with the conventional microscope, display a trembling movement in a liquid medium, and this often gives the impression that the objects are dancing irregularly back and forth. This so-called Brownian movement depends upon thermal movement of molecules in the surrounding liquid and can be distinguished readily from directed spontaneous movement by careful observation. Spontaneously moving bacteria always move through long or short distances in a definite direction, while bacteria which are subjected to Brownian movement "dance" first in one direction, then in another.

You cannot see the flagellae of motile bacteria either in living preparations or in those stained in the conventional manner—they are so delicate that their diameter lies below the resolving power of the conventional light microscope. You can get an impression of flagellar movement with dark-field observation, although even here it is not the flagellae themselves which are shown. (On the whole, dark-field observation is a valuable aid in examining bacteria. Unfortunately, dark-field equipment is expensive.)

Methods are known which make it possible to show bacterial flagellae by staining them, although the flagellae can actually not be resolved by the light microscope. You can do this by depositing certain substances on the flagellae which, in their turn, can be stained. Thus, the diameter of the flagellae is artificially enlarged by a deposit of this substance and brought into the range of the microscope's resolving power. This is naturally a crude method, and the structures obtained might be largely artifacts. Perhaps the flagellae are really arranged quite differently than they appear to you in the stained preparation. In spite of this, flagellar staining is important in many cases, for the apparent image of the flagellae is usually the same in the same species of bacteria. The flagellar staining method which follows[22] deposits an iron-tannin mordant on the flagellae:

Clean a slide (rather than a cover-glass) in dichromate cleaning solution, wash in water and rinse in 95% ethyl alcohol which is removed by flaming. Prepare a smear on this slide as thin as possible. Fix it as usual by air-drying with a flame. Then put the smear in the solution cited below for 15 to 20 minutes:

20% tannic acid solution................................10 cc.
Ferrous sulphate solution, saturated............... 5 cc.
Saturated fuchsine solution in 70% alcohol...... 1 cc.

From this mordant solution the smear is rinsed off with water, stained for about 10 minutes with fuchsine, and rinsed off again. In successful preparations the flagellae are shown in the form of fine threads.

Staining methods are used only to a limited extent in identifying pathogenic bacteria. Culture techniques and animal experiments are usually used in these cases. Bacteria causing suppurations and the tubercle bacillus are exceptions which, in certain cases, can even be identified merely by staining without special techniques.

CAUTION: the amateur should be discouraged from working with pathogenic bacteria. Even highly experienced bacteriologists and laboratory technicians have been known to infect themselves, sometimes fatally, when handling pathogens.

If you feel that you are experienced enough to work with pathogens, you can first examine pus. Smear a small sample as thin as possible and fix it over a flame after air-drying. Since you will usually find cocci causing suppuration, stain with dilute aqueous methylene blue solution (preferably Löffler's methylene blue) for about 5 minutes and then rinse off with water. Either examine the air-dried smear directly by oil-immersion without further mounting or first mount it in a synthetic mounting medium. Since the expected cocci are very small, it is necessary to examine carefully with an oil-immersion objective.

The most important causative agents of suppuration are *Staphylococci*, which lie in clusters like grapes, and the more dangerous *Streptococci*, which are arranged in chains. (But not all *Staphylococci* and *Streptococci* are pathogenic—you can find completely harmless *Streptococci* in milk, for example.) In smear preparations of pus you will first be struck by the countless pus corpuscles. Pus consists essentially of these, which are nothing but leucocytes that have migrated to the focus of infection. The blue-stained, lobed

---

[22] Löffler's method, combined with Conn's cleaning method.

nuclei of these pus bodies can be seen nicely in a methylene blue preparation. Among these pus corpuscles you will find bacteria, which—especially in older suppurations—can outnumber the real causative agents of suppuration. In pus preparations you will often find many bacteria inside of the pus bodies: intracellular bacteria. These bacteria have been phagocytized, i.e., ingested (eaten) by the pus bodies.

Gonococci (*Neisseria gonorrhoeae*), the causative organism for gonorrhea, appear distinctly in the pus smear after methylene blue staining. It is almost impossible to confuse them. They are typical diplococci, i.e., two cocci situated next to one another, especially inside of the white blood corpuscle. Thus, in gonococci there is a typical "coffee bean" image. In contrast to most of the other micrococci, gonococci are Gram-negative.

The tubercle bacillus can be distinguished from other bacteria by staining since it exhibits a property which most other bacteria do not have: it is acid-fast. Acid-fast bacteria have waxlike substances deposited on them, which are responsible for the bacteria giving off stains they have absorbed only slowly in acid differentiating agents; non-acid-fast bacteria lose their stain quickly again in such differentiating agents (hydrochloric acid-alcohol). The tubercle bacillus is not the only acid-fast bacteria. However, hardly any other acid-fast bacterial rods besides it could be present in sputum. For this reason the identification of acid-fast bacteria in the sputum almost always indicates tubercle bacilli. The staining technique for tubercle bacilli[23] is:

Fish a few solid particles out of the sputum with a needle which has been flamed and crush them between two very clean microscope slides (cleaned with alcohol) to form smears as thin as possible. Allow the smears to dry in the air, protected from dust. After fixing with a flame, place the slides in carbol fuchsine and heat them until fumes rise from the stain solution. (An alternative method[24] is to fix them over boiling water.) Let the stain solution act for 4 more minutes without further heating, then pour it off and immerse the smears in hydrochloric acid-alcohol (100 cc. 70% alcohol+0.5 cc. pure, concentrated hydrochloric acid) until the stain is not visible when you look at them with the naked eye. Next place the slides for 2 to 3 minutes in methylene blue solution, rinse off with distilled water, let them dry, and mount in a synthetic mounting medium. Microscopic observations show all structures in a blue tint. Only acid-fast tubercle bacilli have retained the fuchsine and consequently appear to be stained red. Therefore, red bacilli in a preparation

---

[23] Ziehl-Neelsen method.

[24] Conn's method.

otherwise stained blue are probably (but not necessarily) tubercle bacilli. In some cases, only a few red bacilli can be found. Therefore, the preparation must be examined carefully with the oil-immersion objective.

CAUTION: The very greatest care and neatness are necessary in any work with pathogenic bacteria. Even with mere smear preparations, there is always the possibility of infection. Cultures of pathogenic bacteria and animal experiments cannot be considered by one who is not an expert.

MAKING BACTERIAL CULTURES

You have already examined and become acquainted with bacteria from decaying meat, soil, hay infusions, manure, and so forth. As interesting as such simple studies are, they only tell a little about the properties of individual species of bacteria. In order to find out more, you must culture the bacteria—you must tend them like house plants or domestic animals.

You must create good living conditions for the bacteria—especially plenty of nutrients and sufficient moisture—so that they will grow well for you. The simplest culture medium is meat broth. If you fill a test tube with clear meat broth (see page 193) and inoculate it with a little of a substance which contains bacteria—perhaps soil from your garden—the meat broth will begin to get turbid, even after a few days. If you remove a drop of the liquid which already smells foul and examine it under the microscope, you will find plenty of bacteria of the most varied kinds. Thus, meat broth is a good culture medium and serves as a basis for most of the commonly used culture media for bacteria.

You would learn little if you cultured together the many species of bacteria which occur in nature. After all, you want to become acquainted with the characteristics of individual species and therefore must strive always to have only one species in a culture. All other species must be eliminated by making the culture medium and all of the equipment you use free of germs. Let us first deal with methods of making these free of bacteria by sterilizing them.

Sterilization

The aim of sterilization is to kill off all germs and the most commonly used technique of sterilization is the utilization of heat. Even by simple boiling you can kill all vegetative bacteria, i.e., those not present in the spore form. It is more difficult to kill spores. Most bacterial spores easily withstand temperatures of 100° C. All spores are destroyed only at a temperature of 120° C. in an atmosphere saturated with steam. In a well-equipped laboratory, therefore, autoclaves are used to sterilize culture media. In autoclaves, water is brought to a boil under pressure. But sterilization can be safely carried out even without autoclaves. As you know, water boils at temperatures higher than 100° C. at pressures higher than that of the atmosphere. If autoclaves are not available to you, you can use a pressure cooker instead.

DRY STERILIZATION

To sterilize dry equipment in your hot-air sterilizer, the internal temperature has to be brought to 160° C. for half an hour. This is because bacterial spores are not killed in a dry environment until about 150° C. You can make a primitive hot-air sterilizer yourself from a round gallon tin—see the details in Fig. 93. Still simpler: use the oven in your kitchen stove as a hot-air sterilizer.

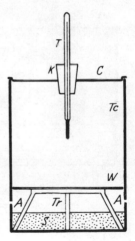

Fig. 93. Hot-air sterilizer. Tc—tin; C=cover; Tr=tripod; K=cork; A=air holes; W=wire gauze; S=sand; T=thermometer. Place the material to be sterilized on the wire gauze, close the tin, and place it over a high gas flame. When the thermometer reads 170° C., regulate the flame to maintain this temperature. The temperature should not drop below 160° C. in the next half-hour. The container may be opened only when the temperature has dropped to about 60° C. If you were to open it at a higher temperature, glass equipment could burst.

(Adapted from Erdmann, *Mikrokosmos, 41*, 1952, 162.)

WATER BATH STERILIZATION

After sterilizing by hot air you are ready to use boiling water to sterilize your culture media. This has to be done fractionally. For fractional sterilization use a large pressure cooker with sufficient water covering the bottom. Place the container with culture medium on a suitable support. If your cooker cannot withstand temperatures above 100° C., stopper it so that it is secure from bacteria (for more details on stoppering, see below). Boil the covered cooker with the culture medium raised above the water bath for half an hour. In this way, all vegetative forms of bacteria are killed, but not spores. Now, if you allow the culture medium to cool again, the spores that are still alive will germinate into vegetative forms since they are in a suitable medium. Therefore, boil the culture medium again in the same way the next day for half an hour. In this way, the remaining bacteria are killed. To be on the safe side, repeat the process again on the third day and with great probability you will have a completely sterile culture medium. The Koch autoclave is especially suited to fractional sterilization (Fig. 94).

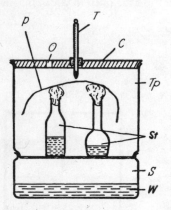

Fig. 94. Koch steamer, cross-section. S=support for holding water; W=water; Tp=top with perforated bottom for holding the material to be sterilized; St= material to be sterilized; P= parchment to protect the material to be sterilized from water of condensation; C=cover with an opening to hold the thermometer (T) and another opening (O) to let the steam escape.

(Adapted from K. Meyer, *Mikrobiologisches Praktikum*, Wolfenbütteler Verlagsanstalt, Wolfenbüttel and Hannover, 1948.)

In this connection it should be noted that housewives could very well be spared their irritation with preserving jars which are always going bad because of gas forming in the jar. If the material which produces gas is boiled just once, naturally bacterial spores can still remain alive, later germinate, and break the seal by producing gas. In fractional sterilization, anything like this is impossible, provided the seal is actually germproof.

Liquids can also be sterilized in a purely mechanical way. For this purpose special filters are used which are impermeable to bacteria. The liquid is filtered through these (e.g., Seitz filter, Berkefeld filter, Coors porcelain filter, fritted glass filter, membrane filter, and so forth). Naturally, ordinary filter paper is not used for this purpose, since it would let most of the bacteria through. But the separation of germs by filtration comes into consideration more for large laboratories and for industrial purposes than for the simple laboratory conditions of the amateur microscopist.

COLD STERILIZATION

In conclusion, the possibility of cold sterilization should still be mentioned. Naturally you can make any substance you like germ-free by chemical methods if you add germicidal chemicals to it, such as formalin or mercuric chloride. But since these chemicals remain in the substance, this kind of disinfection is not practicable for culture media and equipment which will come into contact with culture media. On the other hand, you can also sterilize culture media with readily volatile sterilizing agents, such as chloroform or acetone. Add the volatile sterilizing agent to the culture medium and let it escape again. This usually takes a few days to several weeks. However, the time required for cold sterilization can be considerably shortened by the use of a cold sterilizer.[25] It is believed that cold sterilization methods will be introduced into bacteriological technique to an increasing extent and in the course of time might still be considerably improved as well. For the time being, however, the methods of heat sterilization are still the simplest and also probably the most reliable.

Culture Media

The culture medium used in culturing bacteria is of decisive importance; that is, not all bacteria grow on any old culture medium. In choosing a culture medium, you must conform largely to the requirements of the bacterium to be cultured. The simplest culture medium for bacteria, which also serves as the basis for many more culture media, is meat broth. *Preparation:* Chop 500 gm. of lean horsemeat or beef into small pieces (it is preferable to run it through a food chopper) and boil well with 1 litre of distilled water. After it cools, filter off the broth, add 0.5% NaCl and 1% peptone to the broth, and adjust the pH. That is, culture media used for bacteria should be very slightly alkaline (fungi require acid culture media). In general, your meat broth will be acidic. This can be easily determined by means of litmus paper. Then, with continual stirring, add drop by drop enough 1N (one normal) sodium carbonate so that a litmus

25 Schweizer's and the Ben Venue Ethylene Oxide Sterilizer are cold sterilizers.

paper will just turn a slight blue when dipped into it. If it should prove necessary to add acid to the meat broth (perhaps if too much sodium carbonate solution has been used accidentally), then use 1N hydrochloric acid for this purpose.

Meat broth prepared in this way is an excellent liquid culture medium. You could now sterilize the meat broth and culture your bacteria in it. But as valuable as this liquid culture medium is for many purposes, it is really difficult to isolate individual species of bacteria in liquid culture media. For this reason you will want to convert the meat broth into a solid culture medium:

Add 1.5–3% agar-agar to the meat broth, let it swell up somewhat, and heat it to boiling in a water bath. (NOTE: Agar-agar is a substance obtained from certain red algae which swells up in water and gives a gelatine-like substance when heated with water. Agar-agar liquifies only at about 90° C., which is suitable for bacteriological purposes; under certain conditions gelatine liquifies even at room temperature on hot days. Agar-agar becomes solid at about 40° C.) Agar-agar is dissolved in this way (CAUTION: it foams!). After cooling, the meat broth to which the agar has been added solidifies into a gelatinous mass which is now called nutrient agar.

It must be admitted that even if making nutrient agar is not complicated, it is certainly time-consuming. Anyone who does not want to carry out extensive experiments can buy ready-made nutrient agar. There are a few dry culture media available for general use (not one made for special use) in bacteriology. A dry culture medium contains a powder which is dissolved in 100 cc. distilled water and, after boiling and sterilization, gives ready-to-use nutrient agar. Naturally if you need a lot, it is considerably cheaper to make culture media yourself.

You must now still sterilize the nutrient agar and stopper it securely from bacteria. Put small amounts of liquefied nutrient agar in test tubes (see method below) and larger amounts in Erlenmeyer flasks, taking care that the neck of the container, as far as possible, is not smeared with agar. A simple cotton plug is the most commonly used germproof seal. Of course, the hollow spaces between the individual fibres are considerably larger than bacteria, but bacteria are flung against the individual cotton fibres by air currents and remain clinging there. Because of this, no bacteria from the air can fall into a container stoppered with a cotton plug as long as the cotton plug remains completely dry. Select cotton plugs which are not too small, press them into the container rather deeply, and take care that at least the outer edge of the container is also covered with cotton. (See also Fig. 96.)

To make agar slant tubes, fill 1/3 of a sterile test tube with sterile nutrient agar, seal it with a sterile cotton plug, and lay it in a slanting position on one edge so that the agar solidifies in a slanting layer. In this way you will obtain a relatively large surface for the development of the culture.

You can buy aluminium, rubber, or polypropylene caps and glass cover-seals for culture vessels. Cellophane is also suitable for a germ-proof seal. However, cotton plugs will serve your purposes.

Now fractionally sterilize the test tubes and Erlenmeyer flasks which have been filled with nutrient agar and stoppered with cotton plugs (as described above) and keep them in a place as free from dust as possible until use. It is beneficial to cover the vessels with parchment paper during boiling, so that the water of condensation which drips down from the lid of the kettle cannot moisten the cotton plugs.

Making Cultures

It is best to use Petri dishes as culture vessels. These are flat, round glass containers with suitable, tight-fitting glass covers. Sterilize a few covered Petri dishes in the hot-air sterilizer. Then liquefy sterile nutrient agar in a water bath. Let the agar cool again until it almost solidifies (is somewhat warm to the touch) and inoculate it with a trace of the material to be examined. Then mix the material containing the bacteria well with the still liquid agar by careful shaking or by stirring with a sterile utensil. Then pour this out into the Petri dishes where it will solidify quickly.

This method is called Koch's plating technique. If you have not inoculated too many bacteria and if the material to be examined has really been distributed uniformly in the agar, you can assume with a relative degree of certainty that there is only one bacterium at each point on the agar plate. Naturally it cannot move in solid nutrient media. But it does not need to at all, for it is surrounded by an extremely suitable medium rich in nutrients, and consequently does not have to look for nutrients at all. Under these sustaining conditions, the bacterium immediately begins to multiply and after just a few days many hundreds of thousands or even millions of bacteria are found at the spot where there was only one germ during pouring.

You can even see an accumulation of bacteria with the naked eye—the entire dish is studded with many small, creamy or membranous points which rapidly increase in size. These points, which can be of bright hues or without pigment at all, are colonies of bacteria, each one of which has developed from a single bacterium if you have worked in the right way. Such a colony must consist only of the same species of bacteria, if it has not fused with an adjacent colony or if a few bacteria have not accidentally fallen in while the dish was being poured. The single colonies are then inoculated again separately and examined. But first a few tricks should be mentioned which can be used in pouring the plates:

The air in your workroom is filled with bacteria and bacterial spores. There are plenty of bacteria on your hands and on all of the objects in the room. Therefore, no matter how carefully you may have sterilized your Petri dishes, there is certainly great danger that in pouring the plates foreign germs may fall in which will find the plates suitable, will multiply well, and thus could lead to erroneous conclusions. Such foreign infections can never be entirely avoided, but you can appreciably reduce their number by certain precautionary measures. Leave the cotton plug in the container at the beginning when you liquefy the sterile nutrient agar. Remove the plug with the middle and ring finger of the left hand only during inoculation and flame the edge of the vessel (or test tube) well. For inoculating, it is advisable to use an inoculating needle or a loop made of platinum wire which has first been heated so that it glows. Since platinum utensils are expensive, you can use needles and loops made of platinum substitutes with almost as much success or—in cases of necessity—just wires taken from the heating element of a worn-out hot plate. In pouring the agar, open the cover of the Petri dish only wide enough so that you can introduce the uppermost end of the storage container. It would be a gross error to remove the cover completely.

If nutrient agar is to be removed from a large storage container or if a vessel provided with a cotton plug is used to culture the bacteria, it goes without saying that the cotton stopper must remain sterile. Therefore, you cannot lay it on the table but hold it as you have removed it, between the middle and ring finger of the left hand, during the entire procedure. The thumb and forefinger of the left hand hold the container, the right hand carries out the work involved. Finally, after flaming the edge of the container, again replace the cotton plug. In doing this, it is obvious that the end which was located in the neck of the vessel must be introduced first again since, of course, this alone is still sterile.

Innumerable small colonies of bacteria will grow on your agar plates if you have prepared them properly by Koch's technique. Of course, if you have inoculated too many bacteria, all of these colonies will lie so close to one another that you will not be able to remove any material from one colony without streaking adjacent colonies. It can even happen that the entire plate will be covered by a thick coating of bacteria. You will soon see how little bacteria-containing material you need inoculate in order to obtain single colonies which are separated from one another in space. (NOTE: In some cases you must first dilute the material to be examined, perhaps with a drop of sterile nutrient agar which is warm to the touch.) Before these bacterial colonies grow into one another and thus become useless for your studies, you must transfer them to new, sterile culture media. Use a special culture vessel for each individual colony in which you are interested—of course, each should consist of only one species of bacteria. You should use the agar slant tubes you have available.

Remove a little material from one colony with an inoculating needle which has been heated until it glows and is then cooled again. Inoculate the surface of your agar slant with it. The bacteria will gradually grow over the culture medium and thus provide abundant material for further studies. After some time, usually when the entire area of the culture medium is grown over with bacteria, make the transfers to new culture medium in the manner described. It goes without saying that you must pay strict attention to maintaining sterile conditions.

To determine whether you now actually have obtained pure cultures, you will be concerned on one hand with microscopic characteristics, on the other hand with microscopic examination of the colonies. Rub a tiny sample of the bacterial culture in a drop of water on a microscope slide and examine it under the microscope. If all of the recognizable bacteria display the same form and size, you can be almost certain that it is a pure culture. The plating technique is used for confirmation. Repeat Koch's plating technique (described above) with such a tiny amount of the culture to be examined that it is not even visible to the naked eye. It is noteworthy that most species of bacteria have a characteristic growth-form on an agar plate. Many grow in mucoid colonies, others grow in colonies with lobed edges, still others form colonies of bright hues, and so forth (Fig. 95). If you grow only homogeneous colonies consisting of bacteria which look alike, you can safely regard your culture as pure, i.e., a culture which consists of only one species of bacteria. You can now perform more experiments with such pure cultures. Above all, you can study pure cultures to see whether they display any properties that can be used by man (e.g., formation of certain enzymes, formation of antibiotic substances, carrying out certain fermentations, and so forth). A few examples will be cited below.

A method which leads to pure cultures quickly, but presupposes some skill and a minimum of experience with the microscope, is Burri's India ink point technique. However, with this technique you cannot use ordinary agar culture medium. You will need a gelatine culture medium which is prepared in exactly the same way as nutrient agar, except that 10–15% gelatine is added to meat broth in place of agar.

Fig. 95. Different bacterial colonies on a plate of nutrient agar, schematic diagram.

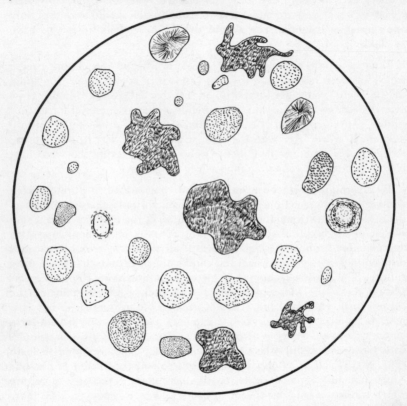

Add 1 cc. India ink to 9 cc. distilled water and sterilize. Place a large number of small drops of India ink on a microscope slide which has been sterilized by thorough flaming. Stir a tiny trace of the material to be examined in the first drop with an inoculating needle which has been heated to redness and then cooled. Then stir a trace from the first drop in the second drop, mix a very small amount of the second drop with the third drop, and so forth. You can now assume that only a small number of bacteria are contained in the last (5th, 6th, 10th or 15th) drop. Remove a little material from each of the last drops with a drawing pen which has been heated to redness and cooled, and place small points of it on the surface of nutrient gelatine. Cover these points with splinters from a sterile cover-glass and examine them under the microscope with high-power magnification. Stab out those points which contain only one bacterium with a sterile instrument and continue to culture them separately. This method is especially suitable for larger germs, while it takes an experienced microscopist to use it for smaller germs.

Both the nutrient agar and nutrient gelatine are standard culture media in which most bacteria grow. However, to continue culturing pure cultures it is often expedient to use liquid culture media. It is simple to use meat broth without the addition of agar or gelatine as a liquid culture medium. Carry out sterilization and other treatment as for nutrient agar. Therefore, it is advisable to place solid culture media in a damp chamber. For example, Petri dishes can be placed on top of one another on a large plate. Cover the bottom of the plate with water and invert a glass bell (or a large preserving jar) over the whole thing. You can place agar slant tubes in a large glass with the bottom covered with water. It can be sealed with a layer of cellophane wrap, such as housewives use in preserving.

An important characteristic of a species of bacteria is its activity in gelatine culture medium. That is, many bacteria are provided with enzymes which dissolve gelatine (peptolytic enzymes). A circle of liquefied gelatine is formed around colonies of such bacteria. Whether a bacterium liquefies gelatine or not can be used to identify the species.

In this way you can isolate, culture separately, and study the properties of an immense number of the most varied species of bacteria from soil, milk, cheese, sewage, rotting substances, fruits, stools, the air, and many other objects. Perhaps the microscopist whose interests are more biological than industrial will specialize on one substratum and study its bacterial flora carefully and in detail in all directions. He can set up a whole collection of pure cultures which must be transferred to new culture medium only every 14 days or 3 weeks and subject them to different conditions. In such cases, two cultures are set up from each strain of bacteria. Work is carried out on one while the other serves to maintain the strain if the working culture should become contaminated by a foreign infection. Questions about their resistance to heat and cold, growth in nutrient-rich and nutrient-poor media, growth on special culture media (which everyone can concoct at will), can be readily elucidated and deep insight into the environmental needs of individual bacteria can be obtained.

The microscopist whose interests are more industrial will approach his bacterial cultures with somewhat different questions. Perhaps from the beginning he will expect his bacterial strains to have certain properties.

It is advisable for him not to set up his cultures more or less at random, but to choose conditions even at the beginning which are suitable for the growth of bacteria with the desired properties or which will even suppress the majority of other bacteria. Since neither the methods of general nor industrial bacteriology can be treated in detail here, a few examples must suffice. The interested microscopist will easily be able to modify the techniques cited for his purposes. Anyone who wants to deal with bacteria exclusively must study carefully the specialized literature on the subject.

Let us assume that the enzyme cellulase is to be isolated from a micro-organism. This enzyme hydrolyzes cellulose, i.e., the substance in the wall of plant cells, into sugar. Cellulase is produced by many fungi and bacteria which meet their carbohydrate requirements from cellulose, common everywhere in nature, with the aid of this enzyme. Your first job will now be to find a micro-organism which is provided with cellulase. In the present case, you can procure such organisms from a biological supply house. It is more interesting to isolate from nature a cellulase-producing bacterium yourself. Besides, there are countless analogous tasks in which the corresponding suitable bacterial strain cannot be procured from a supply house. It is advisable to try and concentrate bacteria which hydrolyze cellulose in a mixed culture. Offer the bacteria pure cellulose as the only source of carbohydrate, but in addition you must put in the necessary mineral salts. As a culture medium, therefore, use one of the synethetic nutrient solutions which do not contain any organic matter. For example, the Czapek-Dox solution is such a synthetic nutrient solution:

Sodium nitrate	2.00 gm.
Potassium acid phosphate K_2HPO_4	1.00 gm.
Potassium chloride	0.50 gm.
Magnesium sulphate	0.50 gm.
Ferrous sulphate	0.02 gm.
Water	1.00 litre

In addition, 50 gm. of d-glucose (dextrose) really belong to the above Czapek-Dox solution as it is usually employed for fungi. It goes without saying that in this case the glucose is left out, since you want to use cellulose as the only source of carbohydrate. Add, however, a tiny trace of malt extract or unhopped beer wort. The micro-organisms need traces of certain substances, which are together called growth factors, for growth. These are contained in malt extract, for example.

Suspend a wad of cotton or filter paper as a source of cellulose in the upper layers of a culture vessel filled with Czapek-Dox solution and inoculate it with a material suspected of containing bacteria which hydrolyze cellulose, e.g., composted soil or half-decomposed leaf litter. Above all, those bacteria which can decompose cellulose, i.e., can use it as a nutrient, will be at home in this nutrient solution. They will multiply rapidly. After some time you can set up a second mixed culture by inoculating a new nutrient solution with a small amount from the first culture. (In doing so, inoculate a cellulose fibre along with it if possible, since the bacteria adhere firmly to the fibres.) Naturally there will be still more cellulose-hydrolyzing organisms among the micro-organisms developing in the second culture than in the first. If you now use Koch's plating technique, i.e., attempt to obtain pure cultures from bacteria in the mixed culture, you may find several bacterial or fungal strains provided with the enzyme cellulase among the colonies that have formed. As a trial, inoculate the colonies which have grown separately on synthetic culture media with cellulose as the only source of carbohydrate and test their propagation in such a culture medium. It is essentially a chemical problem to obtain the enzyme from the culture liquid and the cells. A few hints will be given later on.

It must be noted that the attempt to find a cellulose-hydrolyzing organism has been cited here only as a model for similar experiments. Today this experiment hardly has any more industrial importance, since the enzyme cellulase has been obtained for a long time from micro-organisms in a large-scale process. It is used, among other places, in combination with other enzymes in medicine for digestive disturbances.

There is hardly an organic substance which cannot be attacked by micro-organisms with the aid of enzymes, and many substances which are also of industrial importance are formed by micro-organisms as products of metabolism. Just think of citric acid, fats and antibiotics which man can prepare today from certain bacteria, to say nothing of alcohol and vinegar, which have been obtained with the aid of micro-organisms for ages. Industrial microbiology deals with these matters. It is a young science whose golden age is certainly approaching. Here a wide field is open even to the amateur microscopist who wants to deal seriously with the industrial evaluation of micro-organisms. Knowledge of the specialized literature and a knowledge of chemistry, or at least the assistance of a chemist, are obviously indispensable. But dealing with applied microbiology reveals a knowledge of biology even to those who do not want to penetrate quite so deeply into the field. Of course, it is not exactly essential that you immediately patent every insight into natural events! Anyhow, it is not always the best who turn their scientific knowledge into money.

It has already been mentioned that not all bacteria grow on the standard culture media cited above. In many cases you must try to make the culture medium conform to the natural environmental conditions of the bacteria which are to be cultured. Thus, try, for example, to culture bacteria from fruits on fruit juice agar, bacteria from milk and cheese on skimmed milk, and bacteria from the soil on filtered soil extract with the addition of some meat broth. It depends upon the purpose being pursued and a little also upon the investigator whether culture media should be made solid by the addition of agar or whether they should be used as liquid culture media. Many prefer just liquid culture media, others solid ones. Imagination knows no limits in the composition of such special culture media. Naturally, for quite definite experiments you will also use quite definite culture media which have been reported in the specialized literature.

Mycobacteria are acid-fast bacilli which can occasionally grow branched. Many of them can use hydrocarbons for food. This property is now used to concentrate them from the soil. The basis for the culture medium is Söhngen's agar:

Ammonium chloride	0.05 gm.
Secondary potassium phosphate......	0.05 gm.
Magnesium sulphate	0.05 gm.
Distilled water............................100.00 gm.	
Agar-agar	1.00 gm.

As you can see, Söhngen's agar is free of organic matter with the exception of the agar-agar. (Agar-agar itself can be used by very few bacteria as a nutrient.) Therefore it cannot be assumed that any kind of bacteria grow on this synthetic culture medium without further addition of organic substances. Now scatter a little finely-ground soil on the surface of the agar, place the culture dish in a larger container, and place a small watch-glass with gasoline or petrol next to the culture dish in the container. After some time, colonies of *Mycobacteria* are formed in the vicinity of the crumbs of soil. They use the fumes of gasoline or petrol as a source of carbon.[26]

Quite a few bacteria grow only if oxygen is excluded, and for some, atmospheric oxygen is nothing short of a poison. These bacteria are called anaerobic. You will naturally not find anaerobic bacteria in cultures made by the usual methods. You must keep atmospheric oxygen away from the nutrient medium in order to culture them.

---

[26] From R. Meyer, *Mikrobiologisches Praktikum* (see footnote j, Fig. 94).

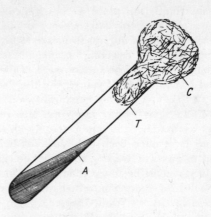

Fig. 96. Agar slant tube. A=nutrient
agar; T=test tube; C=cotton plug.

Innumerable methods are known for culturing anaerobes. Most of these techniques are quite complicated and only two simple culture techniques will be mentioned here.

Sterilize nutrient agar in a test tube, let the agar solidify again, and stab it as deeply as possible with a long inoculating needle which has first been immersed in a soil suspension. Since the canal formed by the stab is narrow and is rapidly closed again by the spongy agar, no atmospheric oxygen is present any longer at the end of the canal. Anaerobic bacteria will develop here, while aerobic bacteria, i.e., those which need oxygen, will grow on the surface and on parts of the canal on the surface. Naturally this primitive method is little suited to the study of pure cultures. For this it is advisable to use the Wright-Burri technique. In this technique, the oxygen in the culture vessel is absorbed by a suitable substance. The culture tube to be inoculated is stoppered first with a flamed cotton plug. The end of the plug projecting over the edge of the tube is cut off, and the plug is pushed into the tube with a glass rod so deeply that it just sits 1 to 2 cm. over the culture medium. Now stopper the tube with a second cotton plug which should not touch the first one. Now drop 1 cc. of a 20% pyrogallol solution on the second cotton plug and next to it 1 cc. of a solution of 50 gm. of crystallized sodium carbonate in 100 cc. water. Finally, seal the culture tube with a tight-fitting rubber stopper and, if you like, seal it in addition with paraffin, plasticine, or petroleum jelly.

Perhaps this is the place to say something about the incubator, a problem which probably affects every amateur microscopist. Most of the bacteria and fungi of interest to us are saprophytes (vegetable organisms living upon dead or decaying organic matter) which grow well even at room temperature. To be sure, growth of the cultures can be very much hastened in many cases if you expose them to a constant temperature of 25–28° C. (For pathogenic organisms you even need temperatures of 37–40° C. in some cases.) However, this requires an incubator which operates accurately, and unfortunately this is costly. Because of this, directions have often been published for building incubators yourself.[27] Without in any way wishing to insult the constructors of such self-made incubators, it must be stated that it takes more technical skill to make a really useful incubator yourself than the average man possesses. To be sure, the experienced "do-it-yourselfer" can be quite successful. But the rest of us would probably do better to let our cultures grow simply at room temperature—or save the money for an incubator.

COUNTING BACTERIA

For many purposes it is important to know the number of germs in a given substrate—in water, milk, soil, foods, and so forth. Essentially two methods, each of which has advantages and disadvantages, should be considered for counting bacteria. In one case, the bacteria are counted directly (e.g., like blood corpuscles with a counting chamber). In the other, Koch's plating technique is used and colonies which grow on the plates are counted. In the latter culture method you will not by a long shot include all germs which the substrate to be examined contains. Many bacteria will not grow at all on standard culture media. But, then, with this method you will know that all bacteria which have formed colonies were viable. If you always work with the same culture medium and under exactly the same conditions, then you will obtain useful comparative values with the culture method.

The method of direct counting can be used only for liquids in which the germs are uniformly distributed. It takes into account practically all bacteria and consequently gives higher values than the culture technique. Note well, however, that with direct counting all dead bacteria and those no longer viable are counted along with the others.

Direct counting of bacteria is carried out exactly like the counting of blood corpuscles (see page 125). The direct counting method is of great value if pure cultures are to be isolated from mixed cultures. If you have

---

27For example, by Hellwig in *Mikrokosmos, 42* (1953), 94.

no idea of the number of germs in a given volume of the impure culture, you can easily inoculate too many bacteria with Koch's plating technique and then obtain such an unforeseeable abundance of colonies that isolation is completely impossible. On the other hand, even if you know only approximately how many bacteria the mixed culture contains, you can readily obtain a suitable concentration of bacteria for pouring the plates by proper dilution of a small amount of the mixed culture with sterile water or liquid culture medium.

The simplest experiment with the culture method, which is nevertheless very important in practice, is to determine how many germs fall from the air onto a given surface in a certain length of time. Besides, this experiment will teach you how careful you must be in all bacteriological studies if you want to be relatively sure of preventing foreign infections from invading bacteria.

Prepare a few sterile Petri dishes with sterile nutrient agar, let the nutrient agar solidify, and now open the dishes for 15 minutes in different rooms. Then cover the dishes again and place them in the damp chamber. The number of colonies which grow on these plates will give you an indication of the number of germs in the air of the various rooms. For example, you will find that many more colonies have grown on plates opened in the cellar than on those exposed to air in the living-room. It is surprising how many bacteria fall into the plates from the air of a school room or the street of a large city. On the other hand, plates exposed in a forest will show relatively few colonies.

Next you will want to determine the number of germs in the water of your aquarium or the number of bacteria in milk. Such media usually contain so many bacteria that it is absolutely necessary to dilute the liquid to be examined. For example, to obtain a 1:1,000 dilution, place 9 cc. of sterile water in a sterile test tube and add 1 cc. of aquarium water with a sterile graduated pipette. Close the test tube immediately with a sterile cotton plug and mix the liquids well with one another (roll the test tube between the hands). Then again place 9 cc. sterile water in a second sterile test tube and add 1 cc. from the first test tube with a second sterile pipette. After thorough mixing, repeat the process a third time and then in the third test tube you will have a 1:1,000 dilution of aquarium water. Naturally the necessary equipment (test tubes, graduated pipettes) is first sterilized in a hot-air sterilizer.

Add a measured quantity of liquefied nutrient agar which has been cooled again to body temperature to 1 cc. of the 1:1,000 dilution and pour it out into a Petri dish. Naturally this additional dilution must be taken into account in later counting. Count the bacterial colonies which have grown after some time. At this high dilution you can assume that each colony originates from only one initial germ so that you can calculate the germ content of the liquid examined directly from the number of colonies. For example, if you found 100 bacterial colonies at a total dilution of 1 : 10,000, this means that the liquid examined contains a million bacteria in one cc. Naturally you will encounter such large numbers only in media which can be considered almost ideal bacterial culture media. In most cases you will not need to use such a high degree of dilution.

MOULDS AND YEASTS

Like bacteria, fungi are heterotrophic, i.e., they are dependent upon organic nutrients. Fungi and bacteria are treated here in one section, because the technique for studying both groups of micro-organisms is

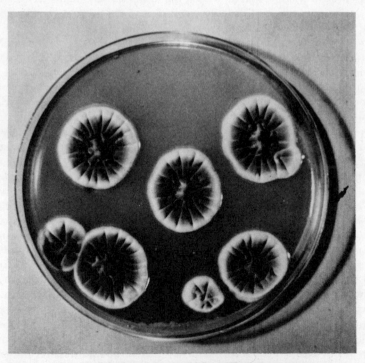

Illus. 15. Colonies of the mould Penicillium chrysogenum.
(Photo courtesy Chas. Pfizer & Co., Inc.)

largely the same. However, you must always keep in mind that fungi are much more highly organized organisms than bacteria and are probably far removed from bacteria from an evolutionary point of view.

Most fungi are multicellular, the individual cells have clearly defined nuclei, and in addition to asexual reproduction, sexual propagation occurs more or less regularly.

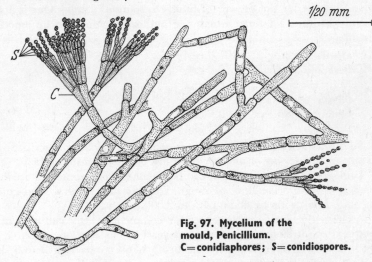

1/20 mm

Fig. 97. Mycelium of the mould, Penicillium.
C = conidiaphores; S = conidiospores.

If you look at a mould under the microscope, you will see a tangle of fine threads. These fungal threads are called hyphae, and all of the hyphae together are called the mycelium (Fig. 97). The fruit bodies or sporophores of higher fungi (mushrooms), which the layman usually considers exclusively as fungi, also consist of such hyphae. The hyphae are closely intertwined and entangled with one another in these fruit bodies so that you get the impression of real cellular tissue on superficial observation. An apparent tissue consisting merely of fungal hyphae intertwined with one another is called the plectenchyma.

The name mould refers only to the external growth form of these organisms which prefer to grow over the surface of damp organic substances. There are moulds from the most diverse orders and even classes of fungi, so that for the sake of correctness this term should really be abandoned. Although it is retained here, this is chiefly for technical reasons. First, you will be primarily concerned with moulds for your culture experiments. Secondly, it is chiefly organisms that grow like moulds which have acquired industrial importance in recent years as producers of antibiotics and other substances. But it must be emphasized here that most fungi can grow like moulds. Therefore, it is almost impossible to give a clear-cut definition of the concept of a mould.

Culturing fungi is done very much like culturing bacteria. To be sure, you can culture fungi, properly speaking, on the culture media customarily used in bacteriology. However, it is better to use special culture media, more suitable for the growth of fungi. Sabouraud's fungi agar is a solid culture medium for fungi which the author has found to be especially useful:

Distilled water ......100.0 cc.
Peptone .... 0.5 gm.
Malt extract .... 6.0 gm.
Glycerine.............. 0.5 gm.
Sodium chloride...... 0.5 gm.
Agar-agar .... 1.8 gm.

Sterilize this culture medium fractionally (as has been described) and protect it in one way or another from loss of water during storage.

Unhopped beer worts, which can be obtained from breweries, are much used as a culture medium for fungi. You can also make a solid culture medium from worts by adding 1.5 to 2.0% agar-agar.

Among other media, yeast water is recommended[28] for culturing fungi. Suspend about 80 gm. of compressed yeast in one litre of tap water and let it boil for $\frac{1}{2}$ hour. Then let the broth stand covered for 2 to 3 days, decant it from the sediment, and sterilize.

It is expedient to use fruit juices for special purposes, for example, for culturing certain species of yeasts.

While bacteria prefer slightly alkaline culture media, fungi grow better on slightly acid media. Therefore, adjust the pH of culture media specified for fungi with a 1N sodium carbonate solution and a 1N hydrochloric acid solution so that the blue litmus paper is just reddened.

First prepare a suitable solid culture medium for fungi, pour plates into Petri dishes, allow the plates to stand open for a short time in the cellar, scatter some dust on them, or inoculate them with moulds grown on bread or other foodstuffs. Even after a few days you will find colonies of fungi which can be distinguished clearly from colonies of bacteria which have certainly also grown. Colonies of fungi are characterized by their thready growth (which can even be seen with the naked eye) and often by a conspicuous formation of pigment. In addition, colonies of fungi usually grow considerably higher than the flat colonies of bacteria.

---

[28] By A. Niethammer.

You will probably find on your plates colonies of fungi which are grey-green or blue-green. In this case, probably you will be dealing with the famous mould, *Penicillium*, several species of which can form the antibiotic, penicillin. You will want to begin by examining this fungus somewhat more closely (Fig. 97).

If you examine a hypha of *Penicillium* under high-power magnification, you will find again and again along its course, partitions which separate the individual cells from one another. It is said that the hypha is septated. These septated hyphae are a characteristic of the higher fungi, while the lower fungi (algal fungi) have hyphae without partitions.

You will probably find small, spherical structures scattered over the entire preparation. These are the spores of the fungus which serve in its reproduction and propagation, and are responsible for the fact that moulds often appear completely unexpectedly at the most diverse places.

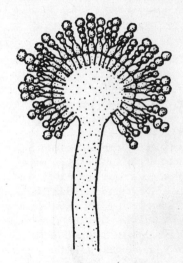

Fig. 98. Conidiaphore of the mould, Aspergillus.

(Figs. 98 and 99 from H. H. Dittrich, *Bakterien, Hefen, Schimmelpilze,* Franckh'sche Verlagshandlung, Stuttgart, 1959.)

Now, how are these spores formed? You will not have to look for a long time to find hyphae ending with heavy branchings. You can see a shorter or longer chain of spores on every terminal branch. That is, these terminal branches of the hypha separate themselves from the outside to the inside into spores which then become free and are carried along great distances by water or the wind. The spores of moulds withstand severe dehydration to a large extent, but are not nearly as resistant as bacterial spores. Such spores as are arranged from the outside to the inside are called conidia;

209

the hypha from which the conidia originate is called the conidiophore. Because of the special forms of its conidiophore, *Penicillium* is also called the brush mould. The so-called "watering can" mould, *Aspergillus*, is related to *Penicillium*. *Aspergillus* also forms conidia, but they are arranged differently from those of *Penicillium*. While the end of the hypha is branched in *Penicillium*, the conidiophore in *Aspergillus* merely bulges out spherically. Short branches which bear the chains of conidia extend from the spherical swelling (Fig. 98). Species of the genus *Aspergillus* have become well-known because of their use in industry. For example, *Aspergillus niger* can form citric acid—a property utilized on a large scale today in industry. Many species of *Aspergillus* are especially useful for obtaining enzymes (e.g., *Aspergillus oryzae*).

Mucor belongs to an entirely different group of fungi. It is commonly found on damp bread and can be taken from there in pure culture. Even with the naked eye you will see tiny black points among the usually snow-white fungus areas formed by *Mucor*. Microscopic examination shows that these black points (sporangia) are spherical bodies which form on the end of a hypha. The spores are formed in them. Thus, in

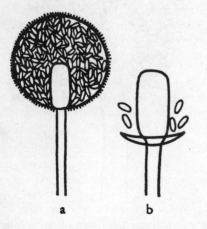

Fig. 99. Mucor mucedo. a= sporangium; b=columella with the remains of the collar.

a   b

Mucor the spores are not formed by external separation from the hyphae, but in the interior of a special body which is called the sporangium. The spores are freed by splitting of the sporangial wall. You can also see them swimming around everywhere in the preparation. The hypha which bears the sporangium projects for a distance into the interior of the sporangium. This final section of the hypha bearing the sporangium is called the columella (Fig. 99).

More thorough observation of the individual hyphae of *Mucor* will show you that here the hyphae are not septated, i.e., they have no partitions. Thus, *Mucor* belongs to the lower fungi or water moulds. You will often read that the water moulds consist merely of a single, multinuclear cell. This assertion is based on the fact that individual cells cannot be distinguished because of the absence of partitions and cytoplasmic boundaries. In spite of this, it is hardly justifiable to speak here of a unicellular organism comparable, possibly, with a flagellate or a spherical alga. It is just in the present case that the cell concept is especially difficult to establish.

It is a fascinating task to make pure cultures and to observe their properties with all of the many fungi which can be cultured on synthetic culture media. You can make a whole collection of fungal cultures (possibly on agar slants). If you then record the observed characteristics for each separate culture on a separate filing card, you will be surprised to find how quickly the cards will fill with interesting observations. Just the single question—On which substrata and under which conditions is this or that fungus able to grow?—will enable you to make plenty of interesting studies. At the same time, answering this question gives valuable information about which enzymes the fungus is able to form. It goes without saying that a fungus can only grow on those culture media which it can decompose and thus make available for its food. Therefore, a fungus which can grow on wood will probably form enzymes that are able to attack one or another of the substances which wood contains. For example, you would test such a fungus for the formation of a cellulose-dissolving enzyme. Study it to see whether it can attack lignin or whether it is provided with the enzyme pectinase which dissolves the central lamella.

Preparation of enzymes from culture liquids and from micro-organisms is essentially a chemical, physical, and physico-chemical problem and can only be treated in passing within the limits of this book. You can obtain the crude extract relatively easily, and in many cases you can work with crude extracts alone. There are enzymes secreted externally by the cells which are then found in the culture liquid. In such cases you can filter off the culture fluid and use it as a crude extract after addition of materials which inhibit decay (toluene, chloroform). The enzyme will be secreted externally, especially if the substrate to be hydrolyzed is insoluble in water, i.e., cannot be absorbed by the cells without previously being hydrolyzed. But many enzymes are bound firmly in the cytoplasm and cannot be obtained without destroying the cellular body. In this case, you can use a trick. Dead cells are subject to a process which is called autolysis or self-digestion. The enzymes present in cytoplasm whose activity

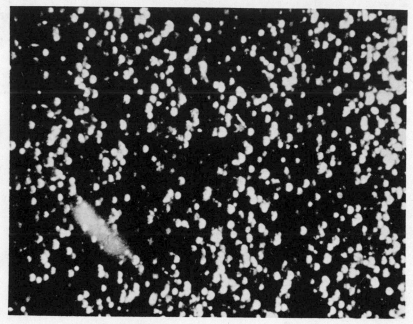

Illus. 16. Spores of bread mould under low magnification.

was strictly regulated during life are suddenly no longer bound by higher regulation and begin to hydrolyze material from the cytoplasm of the cell itself and thus dissolve it. Finally the cell decomposes, and the enzymes reach the surrounding fluid where they can be obtained. An attempt is made to bring about such autolysis artificially in obtaining enzymes from the cells themselves. In the simplest case, some toluene is added to the culture and left to its own devices. Heat must be avoided, since most enzymes are inactivated by this means. Many enzymes can be precipitated from crude extracts by adding acetone or alcohol (crude extract: acetone = 1 : 1). Dry the precipitate quickly under vacuum, and then it is often stable for a long time. In general, glycerine extracts of enzymes are quite stable. A primitive, but occasionally useful method for obtaining impure enzyme preparations should be mentioned here. Microorganisms, together with their culture media, can be evaporated and dried under vacuum at moderate temperatures (30 to 40° C). In some cases a suspension of the dry substance in water shows considerable enzymatic activity which can be used industrially.

It is often just as difficult to identify species of moulds and yeasts as of bacteria, and this must usually be reserved for an expert. It is important for you to be able to decide whether two or more pure cultures belong to the same species or to different species. As with bacteria, you need both the observation of microscopic characteristics and also the growth form of the colonies on solid culture media. In addition, important information is obtained in examining fungi from microscopic observation of their growth.

It is not only of practical importance, but also extremely fascinating from the biological point of view to watch a fungus during growth directly under the microscope. In cultures growing in a Petri dish or even in a test tube, this kind of observation is obviously extremely difficult. Because of this, you can make small cultures on cover-glasses.

For cover-glass cultures you need special microscope slides with a cavity which has been ground out in the middle. Sterilize, by thorough flaming, such a hollow-ground slide and a cover-glass large enough to cover easily the cavity in the slide. In flaming the cover-glass and the slide use two pairs of tweezers which have been immersed in alcohol shortly before use and made germ-free by burning off the alcohol. Grasp the corner of the cover-glass or the slide with the first pair of tweezers and flame it well. Then grasp the opposite corner with the second pair of tweezers and pass it through the flame several times again. In this way, all of the glass will be completely sterilized, even the places which have been covered by the ends of the tweezers. Obviously the cover-glass should not be laid again on the table which is littered with germs. It is best to hold it in the tweezers. After flaming, place the microscope slide on a sterile surface, possibly on a flamed glass plate or, preferably, in a sterile Petri dish. Now stick a small drop of sterile culture medium or liquefied nutrient agar to the bottom of the cover-glass with a sterile wire loop. Spread the drop over the surface of the cover-glass in such a way that it covers as large an area as possible on the one hand, but on the other hand in no case touches the edge of the cavity when it is later placed on the slide. Inoculate the drop of nutrient solution with a few fungal spores (preferably only with one), using an inoculating needle which has been heated to glowing red and allowed to cool again. Then place the cover-glass with the drop on the bottom over the cavity in the slide and add a drop of mineral oil on the edge of the cover-glass. The mineral oil will be sucked under the cover-glass by capillary action. Close the space between the slide and cover-glass, and thereby seal the hollow in the slide tightly. You can also use petroleum jelly in place of the mineral oil. In this case, place the cover-glass in a thick petroleum jelly ring, filling the cavity of the slide before placing the cover-glass on it (Fig. 92).

You can follow the growth of the fungus from germination of the spore to the formation of the mycelium and the formation of new spores directly under the microscope in such a hanging-drop culture. After some time the growth will slow down and finally come to a standstill, because oxygen is quickly used up in the narrow space and the small quantity of nutrient materials is soon exhausted. Then you can transfer it to a new cover-glass and thus maintain the culture.

The various yeasts are fungi which are especially interesting from a microbiological point of view. Yeast fungi usually occur as individual cells. They very rarely form hyphae. Asexual reproduction is carried out by budding. Parent cells develop protrusions which, after some time, are separated from the parent cells by cell walls and are finally set free. In cultures of yeast which are thriving, you will often find whole bud formations, that is, innumerable yeast cells which have formed from one another by budding and still stick to one another loosely in the form of chains (Fig. 100).

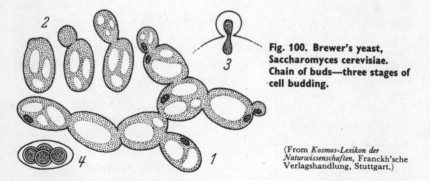

Fig. 100. Brewer's yeast, Saccharomyces cerevisiae. Chain of buds—three stages of cell budding.

(From *Kosmos-Lexikon der Naturwissenschaften*, Franckh'sche Verlagshandlung, Stuttgart.)

Most species of yeast display oval, elliptical, or more rarely, rod-shaped cells. In some cases the cell forms can change somewhat under culture conditions. Culturing can be carried out on the same culture media used for other fungi. Many yeasts grow especially well on culture media which contain sugar.

The best-known species of yeast is *Saccharomyces cerevisiae*, brewer's yeast, cultured from countless strains for the most varied purposes. *Saccharomyces cerevisiae* is decidedly a cultivated plant. As remarkable as it sounds, brewer's yeast is only known from cultures and has not yet been found wild. This species of yeast has been cultured and tended by man for a long time, and many especially valuable strains are trade secrets in the fermentation industry. Many species of yeasts tend to form special strains which differ from each other in one property, and these can often be used in industry. Therefore, it is an important function of applied microscopy to look continually for new species and strains of yeasts and to determine and evaluate their properties—fermentation of certain substances, formation of growth factors, formation of extremely large amounts of proteins, and so forth. If a yeast shows a property that can be exploited for human purposes, it is of value to find a very inexpensive culture medium in which it can be cultured on a large scale without high costs. It is interesting that many otherwise useless factory waste waters, e.g., spent sulphite liquor from paper pulp mills or other waste products, can be used to culture certain yeasts (and other micro-organisms).

The fermentation industry has discovered that the taste of fermented products (e.g., or wine) is affected, among other things, by the yeasts producing fermentation. To be sure, one species of yeast will always predominate in a fermentation which occurs without human guidance (e.g., in wine fermentation the wine yeast *Saccharomyces ellipsoideus*, the spores of which are found in the ground and from there reach the grapes), but still other wild yeasts also participate in the fermentation. This is often undesirable. In modern plants, therefore, the work is carried out today with pure cultures of those strains of yeasts which have proven to be especially suitable in experiments. Naturally, any yeasts already present in the material to be fermented must be suppressed. In many cases, killing the undesirable yeasts by sterilization must be avoided, since the fermented liquid would be changed too much by this process. On the other hand, such large amounts of the desired yeast can be added that this completely crowds out growth of the other yeasts. Work with yeasts also opens a wide field of work in which there is still much to be done by the interested amateur microscopist.

THE WALL MOULD TEST

Knodel has found a simple and reliable test for checking the atmosphere in living quarters.[29] The humidity of the air largely influences how comfortable the atmosphere of a room is. For example, if the outer wall does not have good insulating properties, the air at the surface of the wall is cooled so much that water of condensation is formed, especially during winter.

In order to grow, moulds need a relatively high amount of moisture in the atmosphere. It is well known that moulds grow on the walls in damp rooms—the dust provides the necessary nutrients. This fungal flora on

---

[29] Mikrokosmos, *44* (1954), 1.

the walls is composed of different species, the spores of which are found practically universally.

Apply an extremely thin layer of a nutrient solution for fungi (Knodel recommends highly diluted paste of skim milk and rye flour) to small sample areas on the walls to be tested. If water of condensation appears or the air has a relative humidity of 95 to 100%, fungal development will be visible after 2 to 3 weeks. The most luxuriant growth occurs in the corners. The poorer the insulating quality of the wall, the further the fungi will spread from the corner to the middle of the wall. The more vigorously the fungi grow, the more unsatisfactory the atmosphere is for living. The growth of fungi is entirely absent under good atmospheric conditions. In addition, you can draw additional conclusions about humidity relationships from the rate and intensity with which the mould grows. Knodel distinguishes between the following stages of mould growth: dense growth, light growth, isolated patches, barely growing, visible only under a magnifying glass.

THE MICROBIOLOGICAL ASSAY

Today several strains of microbes have become very important for microbiological assays. With the aid of these assays, you can still detect certain substances in the smallest quantities which would escape chemical detection. The principle of the assay is as follows: The test organism is allowed to grow on a culture medium containing all of the necessary nutrients and growth factors—with the exception of one material (possibly a vitamin), the quantity of which is to be determined. If the organism needs just this substance to live—after all, it can only be used as a test organism in that case—then it will grow vigorously in proportion to the amount of the substance added. In bacteria and yeasts, the increase in number is measured with a turbidimeter; in fungi, the weight of the mycelia is determined and from this, conclusions are made about the quantity of the substance to be tested or about its actual presence.

Unfortunately we cannot go into the technique of the microbiological assay here.[30] Only one especially interesting case will be mentioned as an example of how microbiological assays can be set up:

Thiamine (vitamin B_1) is an activator in the nervous system. It forms in excited nerves and immediately is decomposed again. It is just this vitamin which the mould, *Phycomyces*, needs as an indispensable growth material. A. von Muralt placed excited nerves into liquid air and thus fixed the process of excitation. Extracts from these frozen, excited nerves

---

[30] Interested readers will find a reliable introduction in Mücke, *Einführung in mikrobiologische Bestimmungsverfahren*, Leipzig, 1957.

were added to a culture medium for fungi which contained all of the necessary nutrient and growth substances for *Phycomyces* with the exception of thiamine. The fungus grew luxuriantly on the culture medium with nerve extract, but only with difficulty if no nerve extract was added (Fig. 101). In this way it was demonstrated that thiamine is an important activator of nerves, although the quantities of the material in this case were so small that they could not be detected chemically.

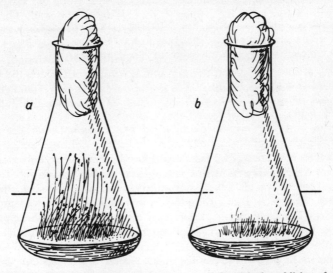

Fig. 101. Growth of the mould, Phycomyces: left, with the addition of nerve extract; right, without nerve extract.

The staining and creation of permanent preparations are much more complicated for fungi than for bacteria. Since in the case of bacteria not much more can be seen than the contours of cells with the conventional light microscope, you do not need to be too fussy about keeping the cytoplasmic structures as they are in life. On the other hand, fungi are higher plants which require correct fixing, careful staining, and careful dehydration. It goes without saying that it is also possible to mount unstained fungal hyphae in glycerine-jelly after fixing.

Fungal mycelia can be suitably fixed in the following mixture:

Iodine-potassium iodide solution 6.00
(Lugol's solution)
90% alcohol....................................... 3.00
Glacial acetic acid............................ 0.25

Bouin's fluid (see page 9) must be prepared only immediately before use, but the individual components can be kept on hand in solution. After fixing (time required: 1 hour to 1 day, depending upon the size), wash off the slide well in several changes of 70% alcohol.

When using Pfeiffer's mixture (see page 10), wash off the slide in water. This liquid is less suitable for fungi which are parasites of animal tissues.

Many of the stains commonly used in microscopy can be employed for the staining of fungi. Chlorazol black E and Ehrlich's, Delafield's, or Heidenhain's haematoxylins (see Chapter 1) can be especially recommended. In the hands of a relatively experienced microscopist, Heidenhain's haematoxylin gives outstandingly good results.

Staining with chlorazol black E is easy to do. Staining is usually carried out in a saturated solution of the stain in 70% alcohol (see page 27). After the fixative is washed off, the fungi are transferred through an alcohol series (20–40–60% alcohol) into 70% alcohol, stained with chlorazol black E, washed off in 80 to 90% alcohol, transferred into terpineol, and finally mounted in a synthetic mounting medium after complete dehydration. The time required for staining depends upon the object and upon fixing. At first it is advisable to stain for only about 5 minutes, then rinse the objects off in 80% alcohol for a short time, and check the degree of staining under the microscope. If the object is still not stained intensely enough, return it to the solution of chlorazol black E. The correct time for staining can usually be estimated easily after one check under the microscope.

It is even simpler to stain in chlorazol black E with the aid of the ethyl ether of ethylene glycol (ethyl cellosolve). Ethyl cellosolve dissolves in water, alcohol, and xylene without the intense reaction which occurs when two solutions of different concentration are mixed. Consequently, you can transfer the objects from water directly into ethyl glycol and from there, without additional intermediate steps, into xylene. (The reason for step-by-step dehydration with alcohol is to avoid damaging the sections as would be caused by the reaction when the concentrations of the two solutions are equalized. For example, if a section is transferred from a weak solution to a strong one it will shrink; from a strong to a weak, it will be torn.)

You can avoid the entire alcohol series and thus save much time with the method mentioned next:

In place of a saturated solution of chlorazol black E in alcohol, prepare a saturated solution of the stain in ethyl cellosolve. Transfer the objects from water directly into the stain solution and after staining wash them off in pure ethyl cellosolve. Next transfer them directly into xylene, and from there mount them in a synthetic mounting medium. The objects must become quite translucent in the xylene. If they appear cloudy, this is an indication of insufficient dehydration. In such cases, place the objects in fresh ethyl cellosolve again.

Even today, staining with Heidenhain's iron haemotoxylin remains one of the most valuable methods in microscopy. If you add exactly 0.1 gm. of sodium iodate ($NaIO_3$) to this solution, it is ready for use immediately. (See page 22.) If you do not, it must be allowed to ripen for several weeks.

It is customary to stain regressively with Heidenhain's haematoxylin, i.e., the objects are first overstained and then differentiated. But in staining fungi, you can also stain progressively, i.e., only until the desired structures are shown to be sufficiently rich in contrast.

First place the fixed, washed, and finely teased-out fungi in a 2.5% solution of iron alum in which they remain a quarter to half an hour. Then wash them off well in distilled water and transfer them into the haematoxylin solution. Stain them in this, checking continuously under the microscope, until the hyphae assume a deep grey hue. Discontinue staining

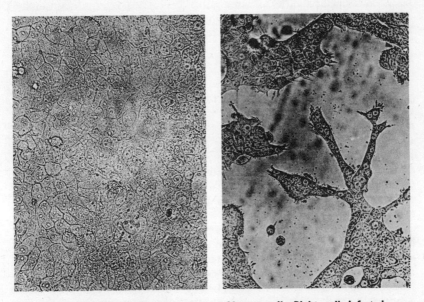

Illus. 17. Left: normal tissue cultures of human cells. Right: cells infected with unknown agent which turned out to be hepatitis virus. (Photo courtesy Parke Davis & Co.)

by washing off in water. Then dehydrate the objects, either step-wise in alcohol or in one step with ethyl cellosolve. After passing through terpineol or xylene, mount in a synthetic mounting medium. In step-by-step dehydration, it is advisable to increase the alcohol concentration in 20% stages from 20% up, so that objects must be kept longer in the higher percentages of the series than in the lower ones. In small, thin objects 3 to 5 minutes are sufficient for the lower steps, 10 to 15 minutes for the higher ones (60% and above).

If you want to show certain cytoplasmic structures so that they are rich in contrast, then you can also use Heidenhain's haematoxylin stain regressively for fungi. In this case, mordant the objects in 2.5% iron alum solution for at least 3 hours (it is better to leave them longer, up to 12 hours), and stain for 3 to 24 hours in the haematoxylin solution. Then the objects are so overstained that none of the finer structures can be seen any longer. Place them again in the 2.5% iron alum solution in which they are rapidly destained (differentiated) again. It is an art for the microscopist to discontinue the process of differentiation at the right moment, i.e., just when the structures which interest him appear at their best. Consequently, differentiation must be carried out by continually checking under the microscope. Stop differentiation by washing off the iron alum solution in water.

SIMPLE EXPERIMENTS WITH ANTIBIOTIC SUBSTANCES

You have probably been surprised by a remarkable phenomenon in your culture plates. If you failed to make transfers at the right time, the colonies of many bacteria and fungi grew into each other and it became difficult to determine where the one colony stopped and the other began. On the other hand, you have noticed other colonies surrounded with a halo which is scarcely populated by one micro-organism. Thus, a substance has probably been secreted here by the fungus or bacterium under consideration, which inhibits the growth of other fungi or bacteria or even makes it impossible for them to grow. Such a substance is called an antibiotic.

Today there are so many antibiotics secreted by micro-organisms that it is difficult for even a specialist to obtain a general view. The best-known antibiotic is penicillin, which is formed by different species of the mould *Penicillium* (e.g., *P. notatum* and *P. chrysogenum*) which you already know. It is possible to consider antibiotic substances to be offensive and defensive weapons in the struggle of micro-organisms with each other for survival. At the present time, it can still not be determined if this interpretation is correct. In any case, antibiotics play an important role in the balance of nature. Because of their great importance in medicine, they have also moved into the field of vision of people who are less interested in biology.

The many methods for detecting the effects of antibiotics are almost countless. Most of them require a well-equipped laboratory, and consequently cannot be considered by the amateur microbiologist. In the following, a few assay methods are presented which, in their essentials, were developed by Fleming and Knöll, but are reproduced here in simplified form because of the limited facilities of the nonspecialist.

On this point you must keep in mind that no antibiotic inhibits the growth of all micro-organisms. Many species are greatly inhibited, others only slightly, and still others not at all.

First, test your *Penicillium* strain for its antibiotic activity. For this purpose, pour a plate of nutrient agar into a larger Petri dish under completely sterile conditions, and let the water, which is expelled when the agar solidifies, evaporate before inoculation in an incubator or another warm place. Then remove some spore materials with a sterile wire loop from the culture of fungus which is to be tested and inoculate this in the form of a streak into the middle of the agar plate. Then, as has already been described, the culture medium is placed in a damp chamber. If you have an incubator, incubate at about 24° C. After a few days, a streak of fungal mycelia will have formed on the streak where the inoculation was made. Now inoculate as many different species of pure cultures of bacteria as possible on the plate, also in the form of streaks. The streaks where the test bacteria have been inoculated are made in such a way that they run perpendicular to the streak of fungus and come quite close to it. The closer they grow to the streak of fungus, the weaker is the antibiotic activity of the fugus with respect to the species of bacteria used. Since you have used different species of bacteria, not all of the streaks of bacteria will grow in equal distances to the streak of fungus. The distance in millimetres of individual streaks of bacteria from the streak of fungus is a measure of the inhibition of a given bacterium by the fungus. If the streaks of bacteria grow as far as the streak of fungus or even into it, you can state that the fungus produces no antibiotic which inhibits this bacteria (or at least it does not under these culture conditions).

If you can find an antibiotic activity in your fungus, the question is raised as to which micro-organisms are inhibited and to what extent they are inhibited. To answer the latter question, definite test bacteria are usually used. Their sensitivity to antibiotics is known. *Staphylococcus aureus* is often used to test for penicillin and streptomycin. The suitable test strains of this species can even be obtained from specialized sources. Pour a plate of nutrient agar and punch out 4 holes in the agar at about equal distances from one another at the edge of the plate with a sharp-edged tube about 9 mm. in diameter. Inoculate a streak running diagonally between each two holes with the test bacterium being used. In place of the micro-organism which produces antibiotic, the culture broth in which this organism was grown is used (e.g., meat broth-peptone). The culture broth should no longer contain germs. Because of this, it must be filtered through a bacterial filter. A small amount of the culture broth, e.g., 0.5 cc., is placed in each of the holes which have been punched into the agar. The culture broth will diffuse into the surrounding agar, together with the antibiotic substances which it possibly contains, so that no growth can occur within a given circle around the holes in the presence of anti-biotic material which is effective for the test organism. Therefore, the streaks will only grow up to the border of the inhibition zone which surrounds the holes, although they were inoculated as far as the holes. You can then determine the highest dilution at which the antibiotic is still effective, and the circle of the inhibition zones will give you a measure of the antibiotic activity. It goes without saying that you do not absolutely have to use culture broth in this experiment. You can also test the inhibitory action of any other kind of liquid in the same way, even the effectiveness of commercial antibiotics.

The following method is especially suitable as a demonstration experiment. The effect and importance of antibiotics can be demonstrated nicely by this means, e.g., in school instruction.

Inoculate a plate of nutrient agar uniformly with a suitable pure culture of bacteria (e.g., with cocci) preferably with *Staphylococcus aureaus*. As has been described above, punch a hole in the middle of the plate and fill this with a solution having antibiotic activity, perhaps with a penicillin solution. After some time you can see how the entire plate is overgrown densely with bacteria, with the exception of a larger or smaller circular border of inhibition around the hole to which the antibiotic has been added.[31]

---

[31] The book by H. Dittrich: *Bakterien*, *Hefen*, *Schimmelpilze*, Franckh'sche Verlagshandlung, Stuttgart, 1959, describes many more interesting experiments with micro-organisms.

INDEX

223